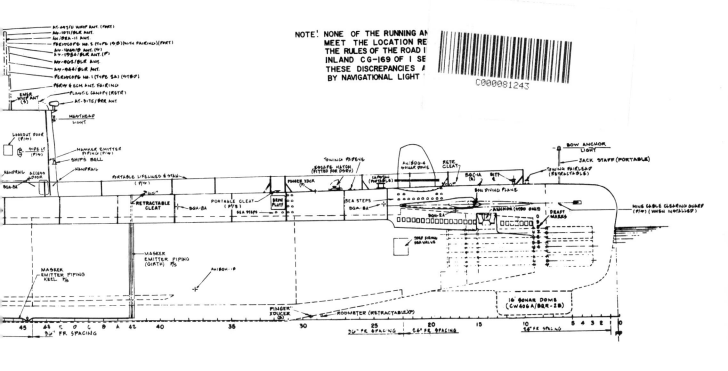

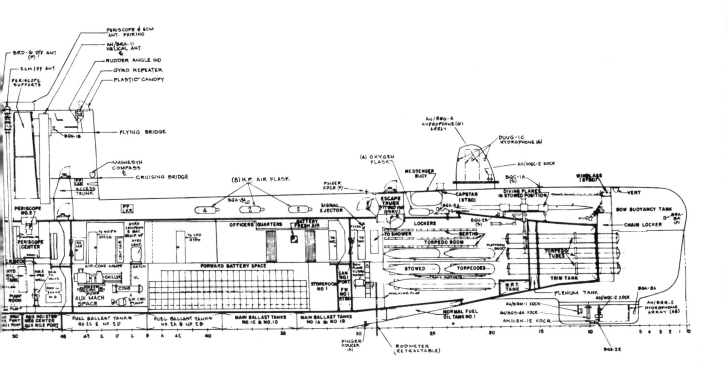

SUBMARINES
OF
THE US NAVY

SUBMARINES
OF
THE US NAVY

STEFAN TERZIBASCHITSCH

TRANSLATED BY M. J. SHIELDS

Bows-on view of *Razorback*, now with plastics sail. The photograph was taken off Hawaii on 12 February 1963.

ARMS AND
ARMOUR

Arms and Armour Press
A Cassell Imprint
Villiers House, 41–47 Strand, London WC2N 5JE.

Distributed in the USA by Sterling Publishing Co. Inc., 387 Park Avenue South, New York, NY 10016-8810.

Distributed in Australia by Capricorn Link (Australia) Pty. Ltd., P.O. Box 665, Lane Cove, New South Wales 2066.

Published originally under the title *U-Boote der U.S. Navy* by Koehlers Verlagsgesellschaft mbH, Herford, Germany.

English translation copyright © 1991

British Library Cataloguing in Publication Data
Terzibaschitsch, Stefan, *1926-*
Submarines of the US Navy. – 2nd ed
I. Title   II. (U-Boote der US Navy. *English*)
623.8257
ISBN 1-85409-145-X

Printed and bound in Great Britain by The Bath Press, Avon.

Photo Acknowledgements

Sources of photographs are acknowledged by an abbreviation at the end of each caption, as follows:

AB	Arrigo Barilli Collection, Italy
AN	Augusto Nani, Italy
CW	Christian Weber, Trier
GGh	Giorgio Ghiglione, Italy
Dr. Gr	Dr Grygiel, Krefeld
HM	Heinz E. Merz, Tuttlingen
LG	Luciano Grazioli, Italy
LvG	Leo van Ginderen Collection, Belgium
INRO	International Naval Research Organization Collection, USA
MB	Marius Bar, France
MW	Michael Winter, Oldenburg
Pa	Pavia, Malta
P&L	Pradignac & Léo, France
RNe	Reinhard Nerlich, Hamburg
SoW	Ships of the World, Japan
TH	Toshifumi Horiuchi, Japan
Te	Author
USN	US Navy, official photograph
WD	Wilhelm Donko, Austria
WHD	William H. Davis, USA
WL	Wright & Logan, UK

Contents

Introduction	**9**
Classification and Nomenclature	**11**
Classification	11
Nomenclature	12
Administrative Organizations for Submarines	**13**
Submarine squadrons and divisions 1943–5	13
Armament	**17**
Guns	17
Torpedoes	18
Mines	20
Guided Missiles	21
Electronic Equipment	**22**
Radar	22
Submarine Radar	22
Fire control	24
Sonar	24
Paint and Camouflage	**26**
SUBMARINE CLASSES OF THE US NAVY	**28**
1941: Entry of the USA into the Second World War	**28**
A Tables	28
O Class (SS-63)	30
R Class (SS-78)	32
Old S Class (SS-105)	34
Barracuda Class (SS-163)	40
Argonaut Class (SS-166)	44
Narwhal Class (SS-167)	46
Dolphin Class (SS-169)	48
Cachalot Class (SS-170)	49
P Class (1st Group) (SS-172)	51
P Class (2nd Group) (SS-174)	51
P Class (3rd Group) (SS-176)	52
New S Class (1st Group) (SS-182)	56
New S Class (2nd Group) (SS-188)	56

T Class (SS-198)	63
Mackerel Class (SS-204)	67
1942-5: The Three Wartime Classes	**69**
Gato Class (SS-212)	72
Balao Class (SS-285)	88
Tench Class (SS-417)	104
1947-56: Later Conventional Submarines	**111**
Tang Class (SS-563)	112
Darter Class (SS-567)	118
Barracuda (K-1) Class (SSK-1)	120
Mackerel (T-1) Class (SST-1)	122
Albacore Class (AGSS-569)	124
Sailfish Class (SSR-572)	127
Grayback Class (SSG-574)	130
Barbel Class (SS-580)	132
Dolphin Class (AGSS-555)	134
1947-64: Fleet Submarine Conversions	**137**
GUPPY Conversions	**138**
GUPPY I Conversions	138
GUPPY II Conversions	140
GUPPY IA Conversions	147
GUPPY IIA Conversions	152
GUPPY IB Conversions	158
GUPPY III Conversions (FRAM II)	158
The Fleet Snorkel Program	**162**
Radar Submarines	**168**
First Attempts	168
Migraine I	168
Migraine II	168
Migraine III	168
Guided-Missile Submarines	**176**
Loon Conversions	176
SSG Conversion of SS-282	177
SSG Conversion of SS-317	178
Various Freight, Tanker and Transport Conversions	**179**

Auxiliary Submarine Reclassification (AGSS)   185

ASW Submarine Conversions (SSK)   190

Administrative Reclassifications   196
AGSS Reclassifications   196
IXSS Reclassification   197

Transfer of US Submarines to Foreign Navies   197

Naval Reserve Force Submarines   202

Submarine Losses during the Second World War   204

Submarine Task Forces and Groups during the Second World War   205

Submarines as Memorials and Museums   207

Bibliography   211

Name Index   212

INTRODUCTION

Currently, the US Navy has at its disposal some 85 nuclear submarines (SSN), but, because of the tight economic policy resulting from a high budget deficit, which also affects the armed forces, there seems little hope of exceeding the magic number of 100, or one-sixth of the active fleet, during the coming years. In both missile submarines (SSBN) and attack vessels (SSN), the US Navy is, in the opinion of US experts, the best in the world and superior to comparable Soviet types. But for how much longer?

At present the submarine branch is experiencing a twofold change:
■ ballistic missile submarines of the *Ohio* Class (ten of about eighteen completed so far) are now being re-equipped from Trident I to Trident II systems
■ attack submarines of the very successful *Los Angeles* Class (SSN-688) (62 units awarded so far) are being supplemented by the next class (*Seawolf*), the technical particulars of which can only be described with superlatives.

All these nuclear submarines have been extensively described in naval manuals and in the technical press. In the German literature, I myself as author have concerned myself with nuclear submarines, especially in my standard work *Seemacht USA* (Sea Power, USA – 1982), as well as in the *Jahrbuch der US Navy 1986-87* (US Navy Yearbook 1986-87) (1986).

The era of the diesel-electric submarine is thus at an end in the US Navy, and this made it essential for me at this point – having already covered aircraft carriers, battleships, cruisers, destroyers and escort vessels – to make conventionally powered submarines of the US Navy the subject of this volume.

I have therefore endeavoured to cover all conventional submarines that
■ took an active part in the Second World War, or
■ were rebuilt after the war, or
■ were newly built up to the introduction of the nuclear submarines.
This covers the history of the submarine over a 50-year period, and falls into four main divisions:

■ A large number of submarines built during the First World War that saw action during the Second World War, with or without modification.
■ Experimental submarines built during the 1930s and later merged into
■ Second World War vessels of the mass-construction programme in the form of the *Gato*, *Balao* and *Tench* Classes.
■ A number of these 'fleet submarines', as they were also known, that were converted for special purposes after 1945 and the revolution in submarine technology (snorkel technology and higher submerged speeds;) several new classes with relatively small numbers of boats emerged as a result.

This book describes 27 newly built classes and numerous post-war rebuilds. The reader may therefore have something of a problem with class designations, which can appear in quite different forms. Here are a few examples:

■ The old *S* Class (3rd Group) is sometimes referred to on the basis of the number of the first boat, i.e., the *S-42* Class.
■ The large units of the 1930s were given class designations on the basis of the boat with the lowest number.
■ The designations of Classes *P* to *T* can also appear as, e.g., *Porpoise*, *Shark*, *Perch*, *Salmon*, *Sargo* or *Tambor* Class.
■ The three Second World War classes are designated according to the name of the boat with the lowest number, but they can also be encountered as the *SS-212*, *SS-285* and *SS-417* Classes. Any further subdivision of these three classes (as may occasionally be found in some references) appears to be entirely unjustified.
■ Classes built after the War are always called after the name of the boat with the lowest number (the lead boat), but here again it is not unusual to find the designation according to the lowest number itself, e.g., the *SS-580* Class.
■ The post-war rebuild classes were named by groups according to the respective conversion type, e.g., GUPPY III, etc.

While working with this material, it became clear that 9

information regarding the affiliation of individual boats to one of the three war-time classes differs between various sources. To obtain the latest information while preparing this text, I made a point of referring to the standard work *The Fleet Submarines of the US Navy* by John D Alden, which is unsurpassed in its detailed treatment of this theme. After extensive discussions with Mr Alden, the numerical designations for the *Gato*, *Balao* and *Tench* Classes as given in his book have been used in this one, sometimes in opposition to quite a few other sources. This is clear in the appropriate columns of the A and B Tables. Mr Alden has written to say that he is absolutely certain on this matter, and goes on to say: 'Because of the confusion and misinformation in published sources, I have made a special effort to track things down in the official Navy records. I also obtained first-hand confirmation from Admiral McKee on most of the changes.' From this exchange of letters, it also became clear that, during building, respective allocation blocks (lots) were often regarded as separate classes by the shipyard, mainly because from lot to lot there were often small differences which affected only the interior of the vessel, and did not have any effect on its overall appearance. To avoid further confusion, this book works on the basis of '*three* classes with the *correct* order of pennant number'.

This book is intended to provide in unified form detailed information on the genesis and development as well as the numbers and types of submarines over a 50-year period of American naval history. This information is given in class descriptions, tables, illustrations, individual information and general text, exactly as in the previous books of this series.

For most classes, drawings to a scale of 1:1000 are provided, these having been taken from John D. Alden's book. I am very grateful to Mr. Alden and to the United States Naval Institute Press in Annapolis for their kind permission to reproduce this material. Some drawings of newer classes were made by Eberhard Kaiser, and a few by the late Klaus-Dieter Schack (*d*. 1986).

I must also express my gratitude to the following for their assistance: Manfred Reinert for his careful revision of several sections; Frank Gerhardt for the adaptation of material provided by Jurg Kursener and Heinz O. Vetters on the administrative structure of submarines; Horst-G Rommel for his hard work in transforming handwritten manuscript into type, Arthur D. Baker III, Professor Jurgen Rohwer, and Gerhard Albrecht (*Weyers Flottentaschenbuch*) for providing photographs; Koehlers Verlag for adding this book to their series; everyone else who helped bring my eighteenth book into print; and to Arms and Armour Press, in particular my friend Rod Dymott, for his encouragement and help in producing this English-language edition.

Finally, I must express my gratitude to those in the picture credit list at the beginning of the book, and to the authors of the reference material listed at the end.

Stefan Terzibaschitsch
Leonberg, Spring 1992

CLASSIFICATION AND NOMENCLATURE

Classification

The basics of American warship classification are given in my 1986 volume *Destroyers of the US Navy*. Starting from the single letter 'S' (for submarine), all vessels from the earliest boats down to current nuclear submarines have, over about 50 years, crystallized into the following classifications – although, more than with surface vessels – changes do occur.

Type	Description	Remarks
AGSS	Auxiliary Submarine	
AOSS	Submarine Oiler	ex-SSO
APS	Submarine, Transport	from 9/42, later SSP
AKSS	Cargo Submarine	ex-ASSA, not used
APSS	Transport Submarine	ex-ASSP, from 1/69 LPSS
ASSA	Cargo Submarine	ex-SSA, 1/50 to 10/55
ASSP	Transport Submarine	ex-SSP, from 10/56 APSS
IXSS	Unclassified Miscellaneous	extracted from AGSS since 6/71
LPSS	Amphibious Transport Submarine	since 1/69, ex-APSS
SC	Cruiser Submarine	only up to 7/31
SF	Fleet Submarine First Line	only up to 7/31
SM	Minelaying Submarine	to 2/42
SS	Submarine	
SSN	Submarine, nuclear propulsion	
SSA	Submarine, Cargo	to 1/50, later ASSA
SSAG	Auxiliary Submarine	only for SS-567
SSBN	Fleet Ballistic Missile Submarine	
SSG	Guided Missile Submarine	
SSGN	Guided Missile Submarine, nuclear propulsion	
SSK	Anti-Submarine Submarine	
SSKN	Anti-Submarine Submarine, nuclear propulsion	to 8/59 for SSN *Tullibee*, but suspended before launching
SSO	Submarine, Oiler	to 12/51, thereafter AGSS
SSP	Submarine, Transport	ex-APS, from 1/50 ASSP
SSR	Radar Picket Submarine	
SSRN	Radar Picket Submarine, nuclear propulsion	1956–1961 for *Triton*
SST	Target and Training Submarine	from 1953 belongs to 'Service Craft'

Nomenclature

In view of the numerous classes which have come into existence since the inception of the submarine weapon, it is not surprising that there have been many changes in the principles of naming submarines over that 80-year period.

The first American submarine to come into service at the beginning of the century, SS-1, was named *Holland* after its creator and builder. Between then and the end of the First World War, more than 60 boats were built, divided into classes which were designated A to N. From the very beginning, the A Class (1901-3) submarines were given the names of fish and other marine creatures. This procedure was continued up to the first four boats of the K Class, where, parallel to the name, there was also a type letter with a consecutive number. In November 1913 the use of fish names was discontinued and from then on the boats went only under their class numbers. All submarines of classes L, M, AA, N, O, R and S were therefore unnamed.

Then, in 1931, it was decided to use fish names again, beginning from SS-163. The resulting confusion over the exact designation of boats of Classes SS-163, SS-166 and SS-167 is dealt with in the corresponding text. Since then, so many submarines have been built for the US Navy that all fish names have been exhausted. Indeed it was even rumoured that marine biologists might soon be naming newly discovered species after submarines, rather than the reverse!

This method of nomenclature was continued up to the introduction of the strategic nuclear submarine (SSBN). The special importance of this type of vessel obviously justified breaking away from this principle, and so the SSBNs were named after famous Americans. The first boat, SSBN-598, was named after *George Washington*, and the last, SSBN-659, after the comedian *Will Rogers*.

During the 1970s the naming of warships was occasionally an expression of the wishes of the current President, or of Navy Secretaries or senior admirals. During the Presidency of Richard Nixon, it was decided that warships should be named after cities of the USA. This may also have had something to do with the fact that at about this time the Navy finally ran out of fish names. The complete SSN-668 Class was therefore named after American cities, but this produced a problem: certain pacifist groups did not want their city to have a nuclear submarine named after it! So Admiral Watkins, himself a submarine officer, decided during his term as Chief of Naval Operations (CNO) that the new *Seawolf* Class should once more be named after fish and other marine creatures. Submarines of the most recent class of SSBN have, because of their special importance, been classified as 'capital ships'. They are therefore named after American states, a privilege hitherto reserved for battleships and nuclear-powered cruisers. Of all the types of warship, the naming of submarines has never been less than controversial.

ADMINISTRATIVE ORGANIZATIONS FOR SUBMARINES

The basics of the form of administrative organization of US warships were given in my earlier works: *Cruisers of the US Navy*, pages 9-10, and *Destroyers of the US Navy*, pages 32-40.

The following survey covers the units of the American submarine fleet between 1943 and 1945, when the number of squadrons in service reached its peak. Most submarine squadrons (SUBRON) consisted of only two submarine divisions (SUBDIV), of six boats each, although there were of course exceptions both higher and lower. The 1945 make-up of SUBRON 10, a Pacific squadron, is striking, in that from its complement of submarines it had the strength of a group and consisted of more than seven divisions. During the War as well as immediately after it, several German U-Boats fell into American hands, and at the end of 1945 they were all assigned to SUBRON 2.

Some time after the War, the SUBDIV concept was dropped and the submarine flotilla (SUBFLOT) was established, but, in line with the elimination of 'flotillas', this was in turn dropped and renamed 'submarine group' (SUBGRU). The organization into SUBGRU and SUBRON continues up to the present day, with many submarine groups under the command of a rear-admiral.

It should also be mentioned that premature assignments affected the nomenclature listed below. It is possible that many submarines completed immediately after the War did not go to their designated squadrons, because the basic reorganization after the end of the War resulted in the elimination of numerous units.

Submarine Squadrons and Divisions 1943-5

Situation from 20 July 1943 according to PACFL Confidential Notice 8CN-43

SUBRON 2
AS-3   *Holland*
ASR-5 *Ortolan*

SUBDIV 21		SUBDIV 22	
SS-182	*Salmon* (F)	SS-185	*Snapper* (F)
SS-183	*Seal*	SS-186	*Stingray*
SS-184	*Skipjack*	SS-187	*Sturgeon*
SS-188	*Sargo*	SS-191	*Sculpin*
SS-189	*Saury*	SS-192	*Sailfish*
SS-190	*Spearfish*	SS-193	*Swordfish*
SS-194	*Seadragon*		

SUBRON 4
DD-336 *Litchfield*
AT-141 *Seagull*
ASR-1   *Widgeon*

SUBDIV 42		SUBDIV 43		SUBDIV 44	
SS-167	*Narwhal* (F)	SS-179	*Plunger* (F)	SS-172	*Porpoise* (F)
SS-168	*Nautilus*	SS-180	*Pollack*	SS-169	*Dolphin*
		SS-181	*Pompano*	SS-173	*Pike*
		SS-196	*Searaven*	SS-175	*Tarpon*
		SS-197	*Seawolf*	SS-177	*Pickerel* (†)
		SS-266	*Pogy*	SS-178	*Permit*

SUBRON 6
AS-14 *Pelias*

SUBDIV 61		SUBDIV 62	
SS-198	*Tambor* (F)	SS-202	*Trout* (F)
SS-199	*Tautog*	SS-203	*Tuna*
SS-200	*Thresher*	SS-209	*Grayling*
SS-206	*Gar*	SS-211	*Gudgeon*
SS-208	*Grayback*	SS-233	*Herring*
SS-220	*Barb*	SS-235	*Shad*

SUBRON 10
AS-12 *Sperry*
ASR-9 *Florikan*

SUBDIV 101		SUBDIV 102	
SS-228	*Drum* (F)	SS-236	*Silversides* (F)
SS-229	*Flying Fish*	SS-234	*Kingfish*
SS-230	*Finback*	SS-237	*Trigger*
SS-231	*Haddock*	SS-238	*Wahoo*
SS-232	*Halibut*	SS-239	*Whale*
SS-281	*Sunfish*	SS-282	*Tunny*

Table compiled by Frank Gerhardt.

SUBRON 12
AS-13   Griffin
ASR-10   Greenlet

SUBDIV 121		SUBDIV 122	
SS-253	Gunnel (F)	SS-259	Jack (F)
SS-254	Gurnard	SS-260	Lapon
SS-255	Haddo	SS-261	Mingo
SS-256	Hake	SS-262	Muscalunge
SS-257	Harder	SS-263	Paddle
SS-258	Hoe	SS-264	Pargo

SUBRON 14
AS-15   Bushnell
ASR-11   Macaw

SUBDIV 141		SUBDIV 142	
SS-275	Runner (F)	SS-283	Tinosa (F)
SS-276	Sawfish	SS-284	Tullibee
SS-277	Scamp	SS-293	Dragonet
SS-278	Scorpion	SS-304	Seahorse
SS-279	Snook	SS-305	Skate
SS-280	Steelhead	SS-308	Apogon

SUBRON 16
AS-18   Orion

SUBDIV 161		SUBDIV 162	
SS-268	Puffer (F)	SS-222	Bluefish (F)
SS-269	Rasher	SS-223	Bonefish
SS-288	Cabrilla	SS-224	Cod
SS-289	Capelin	SS-270	Raton
SS-290	Cisco	SS-271	Ray
SS-291	Crevalle	SS-272	Redfin

SUBRON 18
AS-22   Euryale

SUBDIV 181		SUBDIV 182	
SS-226	Corvina (F)	SS-241	Bashaw (F)
SS-225	Cero	SS-242	Bluegill
SS-227	Darter	SS-243	Bream
SS-240	Angler	SS-249	Flasher
SS-247	Dace	SS-250	Flier
SS-248	Dorado	SS-251	Flounder

SUBRON 45
AS-5   Beaver

SUBDIV 51		SUBDIV 52		SUBDIV 53	
SS-123	S-18 (F)	SS-135	S-30 (F)	SS-153	S-42 (F)
SS-128	S-23	SS-136	S-31	SS-154	S-43
SS-133	S-28	SS-137	S-32	SS-155	S-44
SS-139	S-34	SS-138	S-33	SS-156	S-45
SS-140	S-35	SS-145	S-40	SS-157	S-46
SS-142	S-37	SS-146	S-41	SS-158	S-47
SS-143	S-38				

Situation from 1 July 1945 according to PACFLT Confidential Notice 22CN-45

SUBRON 10

AS-3	Holland	AG-95	Litchfield
ATO-141	Seagull	AG-100	Sicard
ASR-1	Widgeon	AG-101	Pruitt
ASR-5	Ortolan	AG-106	Howard

SUBDIV 43		SUBDIV 44	
SS-198	Tambor (F)	SS-188	Sargo (F)
SS-196	Searaven	SS-183	Seal
SS-199	Tautog	SS-184	Skipjack
SS-200	Thresher	SS-189	Saury
SS-203	Tuna	SS-190	Spearfish

SUBDIV 101		SUBDIV 102	
SS-228	Drum (F)	SS-236	Silversides (F)
SS-229	Flying Fish (FF)	SS-234	Kingfish
SS-230	Finback	SS-237	Trigger
SS-231	Haddock	SS-239	Whale
SS-281	Sunfish	SS-282	Tunny
		SS-411	Spadefish

SUBDIV 103		SUBDIV 104	
SS-212	Gato (F)	SS-217	Guardfish (F)
SS-213	Greenling	SS-221	Blackfish
SS-214	Grouper	SS-286	Billfish
SS-285	Balao	SS-287	Bowfin
SS-267	Pompon		

SUBDIV 105

SS-338	Carp
SS-339	Catfish
SS-340	Entemedor
SS-375	Macabi
SS-376	Mapiro
SS-475	Stickleback
SS-482	Irex
SS-483	Sea Leopard
SS-522	Amberjack

SUBRON 12
AS-13   Griffin

SUBDIV 121		SUBDIV 122	
SS-253	Gunnel (F)	SS-259	Jack (F)
SS-254	Gurnard (FF)	SS-260	Lapon
SS-255	Haddo	SS-261	Mingo
SS-256	Hake	SS-262	Muskallunge
SS-258	Hoe	SS-263	Paddle
SS-266	Pogy	SS-264	Pargo

SUBRON 14
AS-14   Bushnell

SUBDIV 141		SUBDIV 142	
SS-276	Sawfish (F)	SS-283	Tinosa (F)
SS-279	Snook	SS-235	Shad
SS-280	Steelhead	SS-293	Dragonet
SS-412	Trepang	SS-304	Seahorse (FF)
SS-413	Spot	SS-305	Skate
SS-414	Springer	SS-308	Apogon

SUBRON 16
AS-18   Orion
ASR-7   Chanticleer

SUBDIV 161		SUBDIV 162	
SS-268	Puffer (F)	SS-222	Bluefish (F)
SS-269	Rasher (FF)	SS-223	Bonefish
SS-288	Cabrilla	SS-224	Cod
SS-291	Crevalle	SS-270	Raton
SS-367	Icefish	SS-271	Ray
SS-368	Jallao	SS-272	Redfin

SUBRON 18
AS-22   *Euryale*
ASR-8   *Coucal*

SUBDIV 181		SUBDIV 182	
SS-225	*Cero* (F)	SS-241	*Bashaw* (F)
SS-220	*Barb* (FF)	SS-242	*Bluegill*
SS-240	*Angler*	SS-243	*Bream*
SS-247	*Dace*	SS-249	*Flasher*
SS-335	*Dentuda*	SS-251	*Flounder*
SS-369	*Kete*	SS-334	*Cabezon*

SUBRON 20
AS-19   *Proteus*

SUBDIV 201		SUBDIV 202	
SS-309	*Aspro* (F)	SS-383	*Pampanito* (F)
SS-310	*Batfish* (FF)	SS-384	*Parche*
SS-311	*Archerfish*	SS-385	*Bang*
SS-312	*Burrfish*	SS-386	*Pilotfish*
SS-381	*Sand Lance*	SS-387	*Pintado*
SS-382	*Picuda*	SS-388	*Pipefish*

SUBRON 22
AS-16   *Howard W. Gilmore*

SUBDIV 221		SUBDIV 222	
SS-244	*Cavalla* (F)	SS-336	*Capitaine* (F)
SS-245	*Cobia* (FF)	SS-315	*Sealion*
SS-246	*Croaker*	SS-326	*Blueback*
SS-252	*Gabilan*	SS-362	*Guavina*
SS-274	*Rock*	SS-363	*Guitarro*
SS-313	*Perch*	SS-337	*Carbonero*

SUBRON 24
. . .

SUBDIV 241		SUBDIV 242	
SS-292	*Devilfish* (F)	SS-389	*Piranha* (F)
SS-295	*Hackleback*	SS-390	*Plaice*
SS-296	*Lancetfish*	SS-391	*Pomfret*
SS-297	*Ling*	SS-392	*Sterlet*
SS-298	*Lionfish*	SS-393	*Queenfish*
SS-406	*Sea Poacher* (FF)	SS-394	*Razorback*

SUBRON 26
AS-24   *Anthedon*

SUBDIV 261		SUBDIV 262	
SS-364	*Hammerhead* (F)	SS-320	*Bergall* (G)
SS-365	*Hardhead* (FF)	SS-321	*Besugo*
SS-366	*Hawkbill*	SS-322	*Blackfin*
SS-317	*Barbero*	SS-323	*Caiman*
SS-318	*Baya*	SS-324	*Blenny*
SS-319	*Becuna*	SS-325	*Blower*

SUBRON 28
. . .

SUBDIV 281		SUBDIV 282	
SS-395	*Redfish* (F)	SS-307	*Tilefish* (F)
SS-306	*Ronquil* (FF)	SS-401	*Sea Dog*
SS-397	*Scabbardfish*	SS-402	*Sea Fox*
SS-398	*Segundo*	SS-403	*Atule*
SS-399	*Sea Cat*	SS-404	*Spikefish*
SS-400	*Sea Devil*	SS-405	*Sea Owl*

SUBRON 30
AS-26   *Clytie*

SUBDIV 301		SUBDIV 302	
SS-327	*Boarfish* (F)	SS-330	*Brill* (F)
SS-328	*Charr* (FF)	SS-331	*Bugara*
SS-329	*Chub*	SS-332	*Bullhead*
SS-370	*Kraken*	SS-333	*Bumper*
SS-371	*Lagarto*	SS-373	*Lizardfish*
SS-372	*Lamprey*	SS-374	*Loggerhead*

SUBRON 32
ASR-9   *Florikan*

SUBDIV 321		SUBDIV 322	
SS-407	*Sea Robin* (F)	SS-419	*Tigrone* (F)
SS-408	*Sennet* (FF)	SS-420	*Tirante*
SS-409	*Piper*	SS-421	*Trutta*
SS-410	*Threadfin*	SS-422	*Toro*
SS-417	*Tench*	SS-423	*Torsk*
SS-418	*Thornback*	SS-424	*Quillback*

SUBRON 34
AS-11   *Fulton*

SUBDIV 341		SUBDIV 342	
SS-299	*Manta* (F), (FF)	SS-475	*Argonaut* (F)
SS-300	*Moray*	SS-476	*Runner*
SS-301	*Roncador*	SS-477	*Conger*
SS-302	*Sabalo*	SS-478	*Cutlass*
SS-303	*Sablefish*	SS-479	*Diablo*
SS-481	*Requin*	SS-480	*Medregal*

SUBRON 36
AS-12   *Sperry*

SUBDIV 361		SUBDIV 362	
SS-341	*Chivo* (F)	SS-344	*Cobbler* (F)
SS-342	*Chopper* (FF)	SS-347	*Cubera*
SS-343	*Clamagore*	SS-349	*Diodon*
SS-345	*Cochino*	SS-350	*Dogfish*
SS-346	*Corporal*	SS-377	*Menhaden*
SS-348	*Cusk*	SS-378	*Mero*

SUBRON 45
AS-14   *Pelias*

SUBDIV 52		SUBDIV 53	
SS-123	*S-18* (F)	SS-153	*S-42*
SS-128	*S-23*	SS-156	*S-45*
SS-135	*S-30*	SS-157	*S-46*
SS-136	*S-31*	SS-158	*S-47*
SS-137	*S-32*		
SS-138	*S-33*		
SS-139	*S-34*		
SS-145	*S-40*		

Situation from 15 July 1943 according to ATLFL Confidential Memorandum 30CM-43

SUBRON 1
SS-65   *0-4* (F)
ASR-2   *Falcon*
PYc-2   *Sapphire*
YP-12

SUBDIV 11		SUBDIV 13	
SS-63	*0-2* (F)	AG-24	*Semmes*
SS-64	*0-3*	SS-121	*S-16*
SS-65	*0-4*	SS-122	*S-17*
SS-67	*0-6*	SS-125	*S-20*
SS-68	*0-7*	SS-159	*S-48*
SS-69	*0-8*	SS-204	*Mackerel*
SS-71	*0-10*	SS-205	*Marlin*
SS-170	*Cachalot*		
SS-171	*Cuttlefish*		

SUBRON 3
SS-120 *S-15* (F)
AS-21   *Antaeus*
ASR-4   *Mallard*

SUBDIV 31		SUBDIV 32	
SS-163	*Barracuda* (F)	SS-116	*S-11* (F)
SS-164	*Bass*	SS-117	*S-12*
SS-165	*Bonita*	SS-118	*S-13*
		SS-119	*S-14*
		SS-120	*S-15*
		SS-121	*S-16*
		SS-122	*S-17*

SUBRON 7
SS-86   *R-9* (F)
ASR-3   *Chewink*

SUBDIV 12		SUBDIV 72	
SS-79	*R-2* (F)	SS-78	*R-1* (F)
SS-81	*R-4*	SS-82	*R-5*
SS-87	*R-10*	SS-83	*R-6*
SS-88	*R-11*	SS-84	*R-7*
SS-90	*R-13*	SS-86	*R-9*
SS-91	*R-14*	SS-89	*R-12*
SS-97	*R-20*	SS-92	*R-15*
		SS-93	*R-16*
		SS-95	*R-18*

SUBRON 50
SS-220 *Barb* (F)
AS-5   *Beaver*

SUBDIV »x«
aufgelöst, U-Boote
in den Pazifik verlegt

SUBRON 6
AS-18   *Orion*
ASR-12 *Penguin*

SUBDIV 61		SUBDIV 62	
SS-291	*Crevalle* (F)	SS-475	*Argonaut* (F)
SS-285	*Balao* (FF)	SS-476	*Runner*
SS-286	*Billfish*	SS-477	*Conger*
SS-287	*Bowfin*	SS-478	*Cutlass*
SS-288	*Cabrilla*	SS-479	*Diablo*

SUBRON 8
AS-19   *Proteus*
ASR-14 *Petrel*

SUBDIV 81		SUBDIV 82	
SS-256	*Hake* (FF)	SS-485	*Sirago* (F)
SS-258	*Hoe* (F)	SS-420	*Tirante*
SS-259	*Jack*	SS-421	*Trutta*
SS-260	*Lapon*	SS-486	*Pomodon*
SS-262	*Muskallunge*	SS-522	*Amberjack*
SS-350	*Dogfish*	SS-489	*Spinax*
SS-351	*Greenfish*	SS-490	*Volador*
SS-352	*Halfbeak*		
SS-435	*Corsair*		
SS-436	*Unicorn*		

SUBRON 10
AS-26   *Clytie*

SUBRON 101		SUBRON 102	
SS-265	*Peto* (F)	SS-405	*Sea Owl* (F)
SS-426	*Tusk* (FF)	SS-406	*Sea Poacher*
SS-266	*Pogy*	SS-407	*Sea Robin*
SS-267	*Pompon*	SS-408	*Sennet*
SS-271	*Ray*		
SS-437	*Walrus*		
SS-523	*Grampus*		
SS-524	*Pickerel*		
SS-525	*Grenadier*		

Situation from 27 December 1945 according to ATLFLT Confidential Memorandum (Unnumbered.)

SUBRON 2

ASR-2	*Falcon*	U-234
ASR-3	*Chewink*	U-505
ASR-4	*Mallard*	U-858
ASR-13	*Kittiwake*	U-873
ASR-16	*Tringa*	U-2513
ASR-20	*Skylark*	

SUBDIV 21		SUBDIV 22	
SS-214	*Grouper* (FF)	SS-409	*Piper* (F)
SS-404	*Spikefish* (F)	SS-410	*Threadfin*
SS-229	*Flying Fish*	SS-423	*Torsk*
SS-230	*Finback*	SS-419	*Tigrone*
SS-270	*Raton*	SS-424	*Quillback*
SS-403	*Atule*	SS-487	*Remora*
		SS-488	*Sarda*

SUBRON 4
AS-16   *Howard W. Gilmore*
ASR-7   *Chanticleer*

SUBDIV 41		SUBDIV 42	
SS-344	*Cobbler* (F)	SS-480	*Medregal* (F)
SS-343	*Clamagore* (FF)	SS-481	*Requin*
SS-345	*Cochino*	SS-482	*Irex*
SS-346	*Corporal*	SS-483	*Sea Leopard*
SS-347	*Cubera*	SS-484	*Odax*

ARMAMENT

It is easy to form the impression that the main armament of the submarine is exclusively the torpedo, and this is certainly true for the submerged vessel at attack or periscope depth. In the US Navy and among officers responsible for submarine forces, however, there have always been differing opinions as to the role of guns while operating on the surface. There has at times been an excessive valuation of gunnery, accepting the inherent danger to a submarine during a surface engagement. At other times opinion has been that the surfaced submarine should definitely be used against surface forces, while others think of guns only as a means of self-defence or for sinking enemy merchant shipping when the risk is minimal and the use of costly torpedoes can be avoided. As opinion has swung one way or the other, constructional details of various submarines (e.g., deck strengthening, or the provision of magazine space) have reflected them. During the course of the War, another danger to surfaced submarines in the form of attack from the air meant that submarines had to be equipped with anti-aircraft guns. The final situation was that guns and torpedoes were regarded as equally important. Submarine armament was therefore:

■ guns
■ torpedoes
■ mines: used relatively little by submarines during the War
■ guided missiles: gradually came into use in conventionally powered submarines following the rapid post-War development, but were later taken over by the incoming nuclear submarines.

Guns

During the Second World War six types of gun were used in submarines, listed below in chronological order. At the beginning of the War, there were also .5in or 7.6mm machine-guns. Over the course of the War, deck armament went through many changes in almost all submarines, as the photographs show.

6in surface guns L/53 Mk 12 Mod 2

These relatively heavy guns were untypical of submarine armament. Between the wars they were installed only on the larger vessels of the *Argonaut* and *Narwhal* Classes, where they were retained until the end of their active life. They were an adaptation of the Mk 12 gun used on the *Omaha*-Class light cruisers, or as secondary armament on battleships, and had a range of about 24.3 kilometres.

3in dual-purpose gun L/50 Mk 21 Mod 1

A single gun installation such as the above was typical for most fleet submarines up to the beginning of the War. This particular weapon was preferred because it also had an anti-aircraft function, but because of its small calibre, no great results were achieved. Like most submarine guns, it was classed as a 'wet gun' because it was unprotected against the effects of pressure and seawater. Two models were available, the earlier having a higher pedestal than the later one. This version of the 3in L/50 gun had an elevation ranging from −10 degrees to +85 degrees. With practice, a crew could achieve a firing rate of 12 rounds per minute and, at 45 degrees elevation, the range was 13,350 metres. At full elevation, a height of 9,100 metres could be reached. The older Mk 18 model had an elevation of only about 40 degrees.

4in surface guns L/50 Mks 9 to 12

In order to be able to maintain effective fire against armed surface targets, 4in guns were introduced on submarines from about 1943. They were invariably located forward of the conning tower, where they were relatively easy to install, but the length of the barrel required a solid support. This was an old weapon, but was suitable for the purpose and it had the advantage of being available in large numbers, having previously been the main armament of the four-stack destroyers. The choice of a specifically naval gun was the first indication of a move away from the idea of submarines attacking aircraft. This gun had a range of elevation from −15 degrees to +20 degrees, with a firing rate of 10rpm and a range of

14,800 metres at maximum elevation. A few submarines were said to have been fitted with two of the guns.

5in surface gun L/51 Mk 7 Mod 9

This was another old but well-tried weapon, fitted during the 1920s in the three *Barracuda*-Class boats (*SS-163* – *SS-165*), but removed in 1928 on weight grounds and replaced with 3in L/50 guns. They had also been used as secondary armament on battleships. To improve firepower relative to the 4in guns, a few submarines were equipped with 5in L/51 guns from the beginning of 1944, but this was a temporary measure because the new 5in anti-aircraft guns were already in the pipeline. For both these weapons, the deck had to be strengthened, and the working area extended beyond the edge of the deck. The 5in L/51 had a range of 17,200 metres at an elevation of 45 degrees, and could achieve a firing rate of 9rpm. The few L/51s that were used on submarines were replaced with L/25s in 1945.

5in dual-purpose gun L/25 Mk 17, Mod 0.1

The first design work for the development of this short-barrelled gun, for later use in battleships and cruisers, had begun in the early 1920s, but development of the 'wet' version for submarines did not start until 1942. It proceeded rapidly, however, and first deliveries began early in 1944. It was installed during refits, sometimes forward and sometimes aft of the conning tower, and continued during 1945. The necessity for this type of weapon had arisen because submarines were spending more time on the surface by day in their auxiliary role of rescuing shot-down aircrew. The Navy, however, regarded the Mk 17 as a single-purpose gun, because, with a maximum elevation of only 40 degrees and the use of proximity fuzes it could only be deployed in barrage fire against low-flying aircraft. A few vessels were fitted with two of the guns. With a firing rate of 10rpm, the gun had a range of 3,600 metres against aircraft, and 13,200 metres against surface targets.

20mm Oerlikon anti-aircraft guns L/70 Mk 5, Mk 10

Thanks to the foresight of the Navy, the 20mm Oerlikon came into service on submarines as early as 1942, although without armour plating in order to keep weight down. They replaced the small-calibre machine-guns mentioned above. The original Mk 5 version with stable base was replaced in 1944 with the lightweight Mk 10. With a firing rate of 450rpm, these basically defensive weapons had a range of 4,400 metres at 35 degrees elevation using armour-piercing ammunition. At the maximum elevation of 90 degrees, and with explosive ammunition, a range of more than 3,000 metres was attainable. These last-ditch defence weapons remained in use on submarines throughout the Second World War; often however only the mount could be seen, since the barrel was protected against seawater by an enclosure. These 20mm anti-aircraft guns were usually located on the so-called 'cigarette deck' on the forward and after ends of the conning tower.

40mm Bofors anti-aircraft gun L/60 Mk 3

With the advent of the 40mm Bofors gun, the anti-aircraft capability of submarines improved dramatically, although the gun only became available from the second half of 1944. After the installation of the Bofors almost fifty per cent of the 20mm Oerlikons were removed. With a firing rate of 160rpm, the Bofors had the following ranges:

■ at an elevation of 42 degrees, and using armour-piercing ammunition, 10,000 metres;
■ at maximum elevation, and using HE, 6,900 metres.

This exhausts the arsenal of submarine-based gunnery. It is worth noting that because of the limited choice of surface-weapon mountings on the relatively small submarine, no firm rules emerged with regard to positioning. This often depended on the wishes of the individual submarine commander or the practice of individual shipyards. All these types of armament are shown in the photographs.

In the years immediately after the War, deck guns lost their importance, and by the beginning of the 1950s had been entirely phased out.

Torpedoes

Since the inception of the submarine, the torpedo has been its main weapon, and underwater torpedo attack its most effective strategy. Over the decades, there have been many different models of torpedo, specifications varying according to current requirements, but almost all being of 21in diameter. During the first phase of the Second World War, the US Navy had considerable problems with reliability. Many models, which, for economic reasons, had not been thoroughly tested in peacetime, ran deep, or failed to explode because of faulty magnetic detonators, and furious submarine commanders demanded that these detonators be scrapped, which they were by about the end of 1943, although the contact fuzes that replaced them were no great improvement. It was not until 1944 that the torpedo became fully reliable, and the number of successful engagements increased.

Norman Friedman's book *US Naval Weapons* gives a complete catalogue of torpedoes, from which the following list of submarine torpedoes has been extracted.

Mk 10

Used in the old R- and S-Class boats. With a range of 3,200 metres and a speed of 36 knots, it carried a 225kg charge, which was very heavy for its time.

Mk 14

Developed from the Mk 10 in 1931, it became the standard submarine torpedo of the Second World War and remained in use until the end of the 1970s. Range varied from 8,200 metres at 31.1 knots to 4,100 metres at 46 knots, and the charge weighed 292 kilograms.

Mk 16

An improved version of the Mk 14 using the hydrogen peroxide NAVOS propulsion system. Range was increased to 10,060 metres at 46.2 knots with a charge weight of 338 kilograms. It was modified in 1944, and taken out of service in 1975.

Mk 18

Electrically propelled, this model was used between 1943 and 1950. It carried a charge of 261 kilograms, and had a range of 3,650 metres at 29 knots.

Mk 23

Modified Mk 14 with a maximum speed of 46.3 knots, used between 1943 and 1946.

Mk 27

With a 19in diameter, a range of 4,600 metres at 12 knots, and carrying only a 43kg charge, this unusual model came into service in 1943 and was superseded by the Mk 37 in 1960.

Mk 28

This was an acoustic torpedo with electric propulsion giving it a running time of 6 minutes. Its range was 3,600 metres at 19.6 knots, and it had a 265kg charge. A total of 1,750 of this type of torpedo was produced between 1944 and 1952, when it was replaced by the Mk 37.

Mk 37

The standard submarine torpedo from 1956, although it had been in development from 1946. It has a 19in diameter and carries a 150kg charge. Range varies from 7,300 metres at 24 knots to 16,460 metres at 16 knots. It has active/passive homing, and Mods 1 and 2 (1962) were wire-guided.

Mk 45 ASTOR

The acronym ASTOR stands for Anti Submarine Torpedo, and the Mk 45 had a diameter of 19in, electric propulsion, wire guidance, and carried a nuclear warhead. It was developed in 1957 and scrapped in 1976. There is no available data on range. It was the first nuclear weapon to be abandoned in favour of a conventional one.

Mk 48

This is the standard torpedo in today's nuclear submarines. It is a medium-range, wire-guided weapon, powered by a piston engine, and has a range of 32,000 metres at 55 knots. Its operating depth is 760 metres. An improved version, ADCAP, arms the largest nuclear submarines, and can operate at depths up to 1,000 metres. There is no data on the charge carried.

It must be assumed that many of the modern torpedoes listed above are not used in the older fleet submarines.

Some common features of the Mk 14 and Mk 23 torpedoes, which were more or less identical, were:

- diameter 19in (53.3cm)
- overall length 6.25m
- warhead length 1.2m
- steam turbine drive at 8,531-12,123rpm
- running power output 102-340hp
- propeller speeds 950-1,350rpm
- weight of armed torpedo 1,394kg
- charge weight 272-302kg TPX ('Torpex') explosive
- running speed 31.1-46knots
- service range 4,100-8,200m
- maximum range 5,300-9,300m

19

The frustrating unreliability of the Mk 14 during the first two years of the War manifested itself in the following ways:

- torpedoes ran deeper than setting
- charge failed to explode on contact with target
- occasionally exploded too early
- original magnetic detonators failed even more regularly than the contact fuzes that replaced them
- many charges were too light; this was later corrected by introduction of heavier charges.

It should be borne in mind that the exhaust steam from the fast Mk 14 torpedoes left a highly visible wake on the surface, which gave target vessels early warning of their presence. The considerably slower Mk 18 did not have this disadvantage. By the end of the War, submarine commanders were using a mix of torpedoes: the slower but less visible Mk 18s would be launched by day and the Mk 14s at night. There was also the consideration that, at $6,500 each, the Mk 18 was about a third cheaper than its faster counterpart.

Mines

The mine was not a favoured weapon in the US submarine arm because, with two of them in each torpedo tube, they reduced the number of torpedoes that could be carried, and they were neither so spectacular nor so attributable as torpedo attacks.

Nevertheless, many minelaying operations by fleet submarines took place in the Pacific theatre, although, for the reasons given, they are not often mentioned in the literature. In his most recent book on the submarine war in the Pacific (see Bibliography), John Alden notes that submarine-laid mines sank 27 enemy ships and damaged 27 more, whereas the Japanese identified only five of their ships as victims of mines. It should be noted, however, that British boats were involved in minelaying operations which dilutes Alden's figures somewhat.

During the inter-war years, quite a few types of mine – e.g., the Mk 10 Mod 11 anchor-chain contact mine – were produced that required the capabilities of the special mine tubes in the minelaying submarine Argonaut (SS-166 or SM-1). The Mk 12 mine was also carried in Argonaut, the total minelaying equipment of which was removed in 1942. In Friedman's US Naval Weapons, other models are mentioned in connection with submarines, but it is difficult to say whether they were ever actually carried.

Modern nuclear submarines are able to launch mines from their torpedo tubes. Mine types used include:

- Mk 60 CAPTOR (encapsulated torpedo-mine) which is a Mk 46 Mod 4 submarine hunting torpedo encapsulated in an aluminium jacket
- Mk 67 contact mine, which is a modification of the Mk 37 torpedo.

Guided Missiles

It is not the purpose of this book to analyse the relationship between submarines and guided missiles. As can be seen in the class descriptions below, only two guided-missile systems were used in connection with the conventional submarines included in this book. These were the Loon and Regulus systems.

Loon, a US-developed adaptation of the German V-1, was the first missile to be surface-fired from a submarine of the US Navy. It had a length of 8.25 metres and carried a 907kg warhead. The Loon were experimental and not intended for operational use.

Regulus I was a 10.2m-long cruise missile with a range of 500 nautical miles. Its all-up weight was 4.7 tons, and it carried a 1,360kg warhead. It was used in the SSG fleet submarine rebuilds, in both conventional new buildings *Grayback* and *Growler*, and in the nuclear submarine *Halibut* (SSGN-587). An uprated Regulus II with twice the range, twice the weight and a flight speed of Mach 2 did not come into service, the Navy having by this time decided on the Polaris ballistic missile for its developing nuclear submarine fleet. Nevertheless one Regulus II was launched from *Grayback*. Regulus I, however, was an early forerunner of the Tomahawk cruise missile introduced into many submarines and surface vessels during the 1980s, and used to such remarkable effect in the Gulf War of 1991.

A Regulus I cruise missile set up on the open missile-launcher of SSG *Growler*. The photograph was taken in New York City, at *Growler*'s mooring, next to *Intrepid* (ex-CVS-11). [Dr Gr]

ELECTRONIC EQUIPMENT

In my previous books on surface ships, I have placed great emphasis on pictures of visible electronic apparatus, mainly because they can be of use for ship recognition. With submarines, the situation is quite different in that most of the electronic equipment is mounted internally. However, as a result of the growing importance of electronics, it is being mentioned increasingly in the technical literature. For that reason, it is also covered here insofar as it applies to the types of submarine included in this book. The equipment described includes radar, sonar and underwater fire control systems.

Radar

It is known that in the US Navy the development of 'radio location' had begun as far back as the early 1930s, and that the first XAF onboard radar installation was in the old battleship *New York* in 1938. By the time the USA entered the War, more highly developed radar antennae (CXAM and CXAM-I) already existed. Shortly afterwards, newer and mostly lighter antennae were installed on all suitable ships. Submarines would have to wait another ten years for the development of smaller, lighter radars of their own. Nevertheless, only a few days after the Japanese attack on Pearl Harbor, *Plunger* (SS-179) put to sea with the first SD unit on her conning tower, and SD radars were soon fitted in large numbers of submarines. This was very advantageous in giving boats early warning of approaching aircraft, their greatest enemy. They told very little more than that 'something was around', because they were not able to give bearing and range data. U-Boats, however, operating all over the world, would no doubt have appreciated even such elementary apparatus during the early part of the War. For years they would have to go blind against aircraft.

The next generation of radar equipment was the SJ, from which echoes could be read off, if only in linear form. This was a great advance, in that it indicated both bearing and range. The first boat to be equipped with this new radar was *Haddock* (SS-321), in July 1942. Improvements were then made via the redesign of antennae, which also applied to SJ equipment. Eventually, *Snook* (SS-279) became the first boat to be equipped with non-linear radar – in other words, the modern type of radar, which shows a complete 360 degrees scan with the position of the boat as the centre, and not just echoes from one particular bearing.

Soon afterwards, this type of radar was fitted to large numbers of fleet submarines, and to all later models including nuclear submarines. Some of these radars are mentioned below. The corresponding antennae are noted in the appropriate photocaptions, although it should be noted that different types of antenna are often very similar, so that exact identification is difficult.

Submarine Radars

SD
Early-warning radar without exact indication of bearing and range, capable of spotting a bomber flying at 3,000 metres from twenty miles away. In 1941-2, 60 units were delivered. It was followed by several improved models:

SD-1 – 20 units from end of 1942
SD-2 – 60 units from end of 1942
SD-4 – 104 units from mid-1943 to 1944
SD-5 – 86 units up to end of 1944
SD-4 and 5 had a greater range.

SJ
A supplementary model to the SD, the first 160 were installed from June 1942. The SJa was a more powerful unit with the following spotting ranges:

■ battleships at 12 miles
■ destroyers at 8 miles.

The series version was the SJ-1, built from August 1943 to February 1945. For these units there were two different antennae, both tripod mounted. The SJ had one antenna in the form of a 76cm solid paraboloid, whereas the SJ-1 used a perforated paraboloid very similar to, but not as large as, the later SS model. It is worth noting that the SJ-1 antenna also served as the Mk 27 fire-control radar on the armoured towers of battleships.

SR-2

From April 1945, 200 units were ordered, of which only eighteen were delivered, fourteen to surface vessels and the remainder to the first four SSG rebuilds, by which they can be clearly identified. This is an air-surveillance radar with a range for bombers of 110 miles, and for fighters of 70 miles, given that they are flying at 3,000 metres. This antenna, relatively large for a submarine, weighed 1,360 kilograms. They disappeared after the scrapping of the old SSGs just as they were being replaced in surface vessels by the SPS-6, because of poor performance.

SS

The production of 300 units began in June 1945 and by 1949 all active submarines had been fitted with them, replacing the SJ units. Maximum range was 80 miles, and the solid-surface parabolic antenna was 76cm wide. The SS-1 (delivered from March 1950) and SS-2 (delivered from February 1952) had very similar but rather larger antennae, 1.10m in width.

ST

This is a little-known surface antenna running off the power supply of the SJ units. It could be used when the submarine was at periscope depth, and was small enough (5.7cm x 15.2cm) to be mounted immediately below the lens of the night periscope. At a height of only 1 metre above the surface, it was capable of detecting a battleship at eight miles and a surfaced submarine at three miles. Although 254 units were produced from July 1944, hardly anything is known about the appearance of this small radar unit.

SV

This was an aircraft-warning radar intended to replace the SD. It used a 1.22m x 0.61m parabolic antenna on an extensible mast and, at maximum extension, could detect bombers flying between 760 and 4,600 metres at a range of 22 miles. It was also useful against low-flying aircraft: at 95 metres bombers could be spotted at fifteen miles and fighters at about eleven miles. The echo-pattern was read out on the screen of an SJ radar unit. Production of a total of 80 SVs began in January 1945, and of a further 220 SV-1s in June 1946. The SV-2 version, known as 'Heightfinder', was an air-surveillance radar intended specifically for the first SSR rebuilds. The irregular antenna was 2.55m x 0.61m. Only seventeen SV-3 units were delivered between November 1950 and June 1951. SV-4 was a modified version of SV-2 and was used as a tracking radar for the Loon experiments with a 90 degrees rotatable antenna. Similarly, SV-6 was an SV-1 and Heightfinder modification used for missile tracking.

This concludes the radars developed during the War years. The four post-war types, which are still in use on both conventional and nuclear submarines, followed the new series designation (AN/BPS).

BPS-1

Replaced the SJ radars from December 1950, although it was basically a modified SS-model. It could be used at periscope depth, and could detect destroyers at 12 miles.

BPS-2

Air-surveillance radar for radar-picket submarines, replacing the SR-2, and capable of detecting aircraft or missiles at heights up to 21,000 metres, intended especially for use with Regulus I. With its 1.53m × 4.58m antenna, bombers could be spotted at a range of 70 miles. Deliveries began in January 1953.

BPS-3

This was a Heightfinder air-surveillance radar replacing the SV-6, with a maximum range of about 131 miles. It was discontinued when radar submarines were phased out.

BPS-4

The air-surveillance radar used on the *Tang*-Class boats (SS-563), it was similar to the BPS-3. Its antenna was 0.61m x 1.22m, and it could detect a bomber at fifteen miles. First deliveries began in November 1952.

The BPS-5 and all subsequent radars are used only on nuclear submarines.

Fire Control

BPQ-1

The missile control radar for the Regulus I program; it was used in conjunction with the BPS-4 radar, linked via a special transmitter, and could detect bombers at 50 miles. Of the four units produced, three were fitted to submarines – *Cusk*, *Carbonero and Tunny* – where it functioned as a prototype for the BPQ-2.

BPQ-2

This was the tracking radar for the Regulus I and II systems. Its antenna was similar to that of the BPQ-1 radar, and could spot a 20m² object at 60 miles. Missiles could be guided over a range of 350 miles.

Sonar

The first results with underwater detection were obtained by British submarines in 1916. At that time detection was totally passive; in other words, it relied entirely on detecting the noise emitted by an enemy submarine. For some time to come this would be the only means by which a submerged submarine could be aware of the movements of enemy vessels. Even nowadays, passive detection can be more important than active methods, if only on grounds of security, in that the outgoing beam of an active sonar can alert a vessel to the presence of an attacker.

In the definitive works of Norman Friedman, numerous types of sonar are mentioned in the submarine context, but there is no certain indication of when they were introduced or in which classes they operated.

JK

The first American high-frequency passive sonar, this was installed in R- and S-Class submarines from 1936. The hydrophone was T-shaped and had to be rotated by hand. A later version (1938) was designated JKA-5.

JP

A total of 311 units of the JP-1 and JP-2 versions were delivered in 1943, and a further 50 of the JP-2 and JP-3 submarine versions in 1944.

JT

The last of the submarine J-series, 225 units were delivered in 1944.

QBA

Developed in the 1930s, this model had a range of about 3,600 metres. Two QBA and three QBA-1 versions were produced, followed by two QBB versions in 1938. They were installed in *Cachalot* and *Cuttlefish*.

QBE

This sonar was installed externally, on the deck of the submarine; its range was approximately 4,500 metres.

QC-7

A specifically submarine sonar, of which seven were built in 1938. Range was up to 9,100 metres.

QCC

This was a modified QC-4 using the JK-2b hydrophone, and again range was up to 9,100 metres. Two QCC models were delivered (1938), three QCD (also 1938), followed by four QCD-1.

QCM

Used in conjunction with JKA-1, this model had a range of 9,100 metres. Three QCM-1 versions were produced (1941), three QCM-2 (also 1941), four QCM-3 and six QCM-4 (in 1939).

QCN

This was the submarine version with a range of 3,600 metres; the more common version, with a range of 9,100 metres, was installed in anti-submarine surface ships. A total of sixteen QCN were delivered in 1941.

QLA-1

Also designated FM, this was a mine-detection sonar for submarines, with a range of 2,700 metres. This equipment enabled American submarines to penetrate deep into Japanese waters up to the end of the Second World War.

WBA

The W-series sonars provided data on both range and echo and five units were delivered in 1939. In 1941 the WBA-1 version was suspended and became the WDA below.

WDA

This equipment used a combination of the QC-JK and QB systems, and had a range of 9,100 metres; six units were delivered.

WEB

This was specifically intended for use in submarines, but nothing is known about it, except that it was obviously a direct prototype for the WFA.

WFA

The standard sonar for submarines at the end of the War, of which 30 were delivered in 1945, followed by a further 110 of the WFA-1 version. It had a range of about 2,500 metres. The WFAa models included fire-control capability.

BQG

This designation covered a series of underwater fire-control sonars generally known as PUFFS (Passive Underwater Fire-Control Feasibility Study), as were their (usually three) fin-type antennae. Versions BQG-1 and BQG-2, and the still current BQG-4, had three hydrophones, while the BQG-3 had four. Bearing and range of targets up to 13,700 metres could be measured from echo signal difference. First studies began in 1953, followed by prototype tests in 1957. Good results were first obtained in 1960 in *Blenny*. The BQG-2 was installed in the nuclear submarine *Tullibee* with a BQQ-2 sonar, but the *Thresher/Permit-Class* SSNs were given the improved BQG-3. The series version was the BQG-4, which operated in conjunction with other sonar units, and SS *Darter* was the last US Navy submarine to be fitted with it.

BQQ

This whole BQQ series (1-7) was installed only in nuclear submarines, and is therefore outside the scope of this book.

BQR-1

Small unit, used in 1947 to determine range and bearing of depth-charges.

BQR-2

This was fitted in post-War submarines, notably SSKs. Its range varied from 2,300 to 3,600 metres, although it could detect noisy submarines at 10,900 metres. Tested in AGSS *Albacore* and on SSBNs of the George Washington Class.

BQR-4

Exclusively intended for the SSK boats, this was a development of the German GHG unit. Typical of the unit was the faired-in sonar dome at the bow, which can be seen on all SSKs. Depending on conditions it had a range varying from 8,200 to 27,000 metres.

BQR-5

Little is known about this passive sonar from the year 1949.

BQS-4

This was a submarine version of the SQS-4 sonar used in surface vessels. It was introduced in 1959, and its typical range was between 5,500 and 7,300 metres.

Many other types of sonar are used in nuclear submarines.

PAINT AND CAMOUFLAGE

Just about everything that needed to be said on the aims and objectives of color in general and the various aspects of camouflage of American ships was covered in my earlier book *Destroyers of the US Navy*. By and large, similar considerations apply to the color and camouflage of submarines, right up to the present day. There are however special considerations regarding submarine color schemes in that they have different camouflage requirements while surfaced, as opposed to while operating just below the surface.

In the 1930s submarines were painted the normal 'light gray', but, on the basis of experience both at home and abroad, this was changed to total black as American entry into the War approached. Then, in 1941, camouflage instructions were issued for all warships. Those for submarines were based on extensive tests carried out off Key West and in the Panama Canal Zone, and introduced the 'Measure 9' dull black for all boats. It was followed by the introduction, in mid 1942, of the 'Measure 10' ocean gray, although Measure 9 still remained in use.

By 1944, the advantages of multi-colored camouflage for surface shipping had become clear. This was applied to submarines in the form of Measure 32, which incorporated two very similar color patterns. It should be noted that there were always separate directives for submarine color schemes.

The following is the series of camouflage schemes introduced on submarines from 1941.

Measure 9

The entire hull above the waterline was painted black, including all external tackle, radio equipment, etc. This was very effective against detection from the air while the boat was on the surface or submerged, but less so against surface vessels. At first, black gloss paint was used, but this quickly became matt in service, and so matt paint was used from then on. Also, from the tests mentioned above, it had become apparent that a very dark-blue paint gave greater protection against detection from the air than the black. After a few weeks, however the blue paint faded to a milky film, whereas the black paint lasted for several months before fading.

Measure 10

This scheme, released in mid-June 1942, was also a single-color camouflage, but it replaced black with ocean gray. In comparison with Measure 9, this had the effect of reducing visibility during surface operation, at the expense of somewhat greater visibility from the air while submerged. It was especially useful in areas where there was less risk of aerial attack, although it was not very practical for surface operations at night. One submarine commander reported that his boat (*Tirante*) stood out 'like a snowman in a coal cellar' during a night action where there was a lot of illumination. Wartime photographs often show black deck paint on Scheme-10 boats, although there was nothing to this effect in the directives.

Measure 32/3SS-B

Although it used more than one color, Measure 32 as applied to submarines did not produce the many different patterns that it did in surface ships, where it was generally called 'dazzle-pattern'. Pattern 3SS-B was known as 'light-gray pattern', although in practice light-gray was used only on the forward part of the hull. The scheme had advantages in surface operations, especially at night, but was quite complicated to apply. The deck was black, as were all horizontal surfaces, with the transition to the light-gray verticals painted in different shades of gray without firm separation. Immediately aft of the conning tower, the light-gray of the verticals was blended via medium- and dark-gray to black at the stern. The forward section of the conning tower was painted medium-gray. Upper surfaces of guns were black, lower parts light-gray, and the under-surfaces of conning tower overhangs were white. In all, seven intermediate shades between white and black were used in this Scheme.

Measure 32/9SS

The details of this scheme are similar to those of

Measure 32/3SS-B, except that the light-gray is replaced by a darker gray. For this reason, it was known as the 'dark-gray pattern'. It must be noted, however, that specified colors were not always precisely adhered to in either scheme.

Post-War Paintwork

In March 1953 ship color schemes reverted to peacetime conditions, using 'peace gray' according to the newly established Measure US17. Although, in the age of radar, the necessity of paint camouflage is not so vital, the instructions of March 1953 provided for small variations in the basic scheme for individual types of submarine. Thus there were sub-schemes for GUPPY rebuilds (17G), fleet snorkels (17F), and submarine tankers (170).

Unfortunately, there is no firm information on the exact details of post-War ship color schemes, but it is known that, despite the instructions of March 1953, matt black paintwork soon became universal on submarines. Today, all American nuclear submarines are painted in this way.

Bluegill (SS-242), with Measure 32 camouflage, and – a typically SS boat – radar antenna high on the mast, in 1943. [USN]

Mingo (SS-260) in Measure 32 camouflage, 6 July 1955. [USN]

Submarine Classes of the US Navy

1941: ENTRY OF THE USA INTO THE SECOND WORLD WAR

In December 1941 the USA had more than 112 submarines in service, of which more than fifty per cent (65) dated from the time of or shortly after the First World War. They consisted of boats of the O and R Classes, plus four groups of the old S Class. Thirty-one units of these classes had been transferred to the reserve during the 1930s, but returned to active service as the political and military crisis deepened in 1940-1. The remaining 34 units saw continuous service from their launch in the early 1920s until they met their various fates between 1942 and 1945. Under the constant threat of a confrontation with Imperial Japan, the American submarine branch was transformed from a coastal to an ocean-going force, based initially in Hawaii, and later in the Philippines. The old coastal submarines lacked the range for this ocean-going function, which led to the design during the 1920s of the much larger V-boats.

During the inter-War years, there were of course other criteria than a simple desire to achieve greater range. What is true of warships in general is also true of submarines: the more the better. This ambition was hindered, however, by the various naval treaties; after the London Naval Treaty of 1930, for example, the US submarine fleet was limited to 52,700 tons. Individual submarines were limited to 2,000 tons surface displacement, and guns were restricted to 13cm calibre. In 1930, the fleet of 122 submarines totalled 81,000 tons, with a further 10,170 tons building, so that a sharp cut was necessary. The need therefore was to optimize building so as to obtain the maximum number of new vessels within the context of tonnage limitations, which resulted in the designs of the Porpoise Class and the new S and T classes.

A major step along this road was provided in 1933 by the development of the high-speed diesel. Although there were disadvantages, it made diesel-electric drive possible without gearing; the diesel was directly coupled to the generator, and the electric motors were used for propulsion both on and below the surface, using battery power while submerged.

The pre-War design of the P, S and T Classes stabilized fleet submarine parameters at around 2,000 tons submerged displacement, 93 metres length, and 11,000 nautical miles' range at 10 knots. Details are given in individual class descriptions.

The experience of these three classes led directly to the building of the succeeding Gato Class. By December 1941 some 32 Gato boats were under construction, and the building of a further 41 had been approved by Congress.

A Tables (Building Dates, War Losses, Reclassifications, Transfers to Foreign Fleets, Stricken Vessels)

There is a Table A for each class. Within the class, data on each boat is given in order of pennant number. Data on fiscal year of building authorization, building yard, keel-laying, launching and commissioning correspond with those given in the appropriate literature.

The definitive name of the vessel is given in the name column, and this did not normally change throughout its service life. Some submarines had – at least temporarily – names that consisted of a letter-number combination only. These had nothing to do with the official 'SS' designation. Some of these vessels were given 'proper' names at a later date. The name column also gives data on ex-names. These were mainly associated with war building programs, and were not normally given to the submarines. They were allocated for planning purposes, and were usually deleted before the keel was laid.

Many submarines, after their first decommissioning, were in and out of service as many as three times. These individual stages are indicated by one to three asterisks, where this information, because of space limitations, sometimes has had to spread into neighbouring columns.

The dates in the 'War and Other Losses' columns correspond to those in the section 'Submarine Losses in the Second World War'. Losses through causes other than war are shown in parentheses and the word 'Bikini' indicates that the loss was as a result of nuclear tests in 1946.

Many submarines, especially those of the three wartime classes, were reclassified up to four times, and this is shown in the 'Reclassified' column, together with month and year of reclassification. A full list of the class letters, which often stand for the same or similar categories, will be found at the beginning of this book, in the section on 'Classification'. In the 'Transferred' column the month, year and destination of transfer are listed. The name given by the new fleet will be found at the end of the book in the section 'Transfers of US Submarines to Foreign Fleets'.

The penultimate column contains the date on which the name of a vessel was formally stricken from the 'Naval Vessel Register' (NVR). For submarines lost during the War, there is usually no formal deletion date.

The final column, 'Remarks', is mainly used to note:

■ repeated periods in and out of service
■ year of *commencement* of activity as Naval Reserve Training Force (NRT) training vessel, often as a stationary hulk (indicated by NRT)
■ year and mode of GUPPY conversion of wartime class submarines (indicated by the letter 'G'). The abbreviation 'FL' indicates fleet snorkel modification.

O Class (SS-63)

The eight O-Class boats were among the oldest American submarines, dating from the time of the First World War, yet had a service life extending right through to the end of the Second. After their first period of active service from 1918, all these vessels, together with quite a few sister-ships, were decommissioned in the middle of 1931. When it became apparent that the USA would be involved in war yet again, there was an urgent need for additional vessels for the Submarine Training Command and the eight O-Class boats were reactivated between January and April 1941. With the surrender of Germany in the spring of 1945, seven of the eight boats were taken out of service, and later formally deleted. The eighth boat, O-9, had been lost with 33 crew in a diving test on 20 June 1941. Three units were transferred to the British Royal Navy in 1941-2.

O Class

Pennant numbers SS	Ships in the class		displacement surfaced submerged	Dimensions m			Output HP	Speed kn	Range Sm/kn	Oil fuel ts	Complement Officers/ enlisted	Original combat systems
	planned	completed		length	beam	draught						
63 – 65		8	521	52,6	5,5	4,4	Diesel 880	14	4000_{11}	82,9	2/27	1 – 3in L/23
67 – 71			629	Operating depth 61m			E-Motor 740	10,5	50_5			4 Bow Torpedo Tubes 18in (8 Torpedoes)

Submarine O-3 wearing pennant number SS-64. [USN]

Pennant number	Name	FY	Building yard	Keel laid	launched	commissioned / decommissioned	war (and other) loss	reclassified	transferred to	stricken	Remarks
63	*O-2*		Puget Sound NS	27. 7. 17	24. 5. 18	19. 10. 18 / 25. 6. 31				11. 8. 45	3. 2. 41 / 26. 7. 45
64	*O-3*		Fore River	2. 12. 16	27. 9. 17	13. 6. 18 / 6. 6. 31				11. 10. 45	3. 2. 41 / 11. 9. 45
65	*O-4*		Fore River	4. 12. 16	20. 10. 17	28. 5. 18 / 3. 6. 31				11. 10. 45	29. 1. 41 / 20. 9. 45
67	*O-6*		Fore River	6. 12. 16	25. 11. 17	12. 6. 18 / 9. 6. 31				11. 9. 45	4. 2. 41 / 11. 9. 45
68	*O-7*		Fore River	14. 2. 17	16. 12. 17	4. 7. 18 / 1. 7. 31				11. 7. 45	12. 7. 41 / 2. 2. 45
69	*O-8*		Fore River	27. 2. 17	31. 12. 17	11. 7. 18 / 27. 5. 31				11. 10. 45	28. 4. 41 / 11. 9. 45
70	*O-9*		Fore River	15. 2. 17	27. 1. 18	27. 7. 18 / 25. 6. 31	(20. 6. 41)			23. 10. 41	
71	*O-10*		Fore River	27. 2. 17	21. 2. 18	17. 8. 18 / 25. 6. 31				11. 10. 45	10. 3. 41 / 10. 9. 45

Submarine *O-4*. (SS-65)

R Class (SS-78)

From 1917 to 1919 a total of 27 R-Class submarines came into service. Of these, *R-21* to *R-27* were stricken in 1930, but the remaining nineteen units of the first group of this class saw service during the War. Although these boats were only slightly younger and larger than those of the O Class, they were given considerably different tasks during the War. In the early 1930s, thirteen units had been transferred to the reserve fleet; the remaining six served continuously until the last days of the War. Their main task was surveillance along the Atlantic seaboard of the USA and here the principal danger was U-boats. The other thirteen units were therefore taken out of reserve during 1940-1. Their function remained that of surveillance because at that time the USA had still not officially entered the War. Despite their short range, these little boats proved themselves in the mission assigned to them. As well as guarding the coastline from the Canadian border to the Canal Zone, they served as training vessels in the Submarine Training School at New London, in the Sonar Training Unit at Key West, and in various diving training units. They also took part in anti-submarine training exercises. Three units of this class were transferred to the British submarine fleet in 1941-2, one of which was lost in a collision. Also, in 1943, *R-12* was lost due to flooding; she sank within fifteen seconds and took 42 crew down with her. After the surrender of Germany, the remaining boats were stood down and sold. The slightly greater length of the R-Class boats arose from the need to have longer torpedo tubes of 21in diameter, as opposed to the 18in of the O-Class. The US Navy has retained that diameter up to the present day.

R Class

Pennant numbers	Ships in the class		displacement surfaced	Dimensions m			Output HP	Speed kn	Range Sm/kn	Oil fuel ts	Complement	Original combat systems
SS	planned	completed	submerged	length	beam	draught					Officers/ enlisted	
78 – 84		19	569	56,8	5,5	4,4	Diesel 1200	13,5	3700$_{10}$	71,5	2/27	1 – 3in L/50 4 bow torpedo tubes 21in (8 Torpedoes)
86 – 97			680	Operating depth 61 m			electric motors 934	10,5	100$_{10}$			

 *R-1* Class.

R-1 (SS-78) in a 1942 Navy identification photograph. The small size of these boats is apparent from the fairly small 20mm AA cannon. [USN]

Pennant number	Name	FY	Building yard	Keel laid	launched	commissioned / decommissioned	war (and other) loss	reclassified	transferred to	stricken	Remarks
78	R-1		Fore River	16. 10. 17	24. 8. 18	16. 12. 18 / 1. 5. 31				10. 11. 45	16. 10. 40 / 20. 9. 45
79	R-2		Fore River	16. 10. 17	23. 9. 18	24. 1. 19 / 10. 5. 45				2. 6. 45	
80	R-3		Fore River	11. 12. 17	18. 1. 19	17. 4. 19 / 10. 8. 34			11/41 = RN	7. 11. 41	19. 8. 40 / 4. 11. 41
81	R-4		Fore River	16. 10. 17	26. 10. 18	28. 3. 19 / 18. 6. 45				11. 7. 45	
82	R-5		Fore River	16. 10. 17	24. 11. 18	15. 4. 19 / 30. 6. 32				11. 10. 45	19. 8. 40 / 14. 9. 45
83	R-6		Fore River	17. 12. 17	1. 3. 19	1. 5. 19 / 4. 5. 31				11. 10. 45	15. 11. 40 / 27. 9. 45
84	R-7		Fore River	6. 12. 17	5. 4. 19	12. 6. 19 / 2. 5. 31				11. 10. 45	14. 3. 41 / 14. 9. 45
86	R-9		Fore River	6. 3. 18	24. 5. 19	30. 7. 19 / 2. 5. 31				11. 10. 45	14. 3. 41 / 25. 9. 45
87	R-10		Fore River	21. 3. 18	28. 6. 19	20. 8. 19 / 18. 6. 45				11. 7. 45	
88	R-11		Fore River	18. 3. 18	22. 7. 19	5. 9. 19 / 5. 9. 45				11. 10. 45	
89	R-12		Fore River	28. 3. 18	15. 8. 19	23. 9. 19 / 7. 12. 32	(12. 6. 43)			6. 7. 43	16. 10. 40
90	R-13		Fore River	27. 3. 18	27. 8. 19	17. 10. 19 / 14. 9. 45				11. 10. 45	
91	R-14		Fore River	6. 11. 18	10. 10. 29	24. 12. 19 / 7. 5. 45				19. 9. 45	
92	R-15		Union Iron Works	30. 4. 17	10. 12. 17	27. 7. 18 / 7. 5. 31				11. 10. 45	1. 4. 40 / 17. 9. 45
93	R-16		Union Iron Works	26. 4. 17	15. 12. 17	5. 8. 18 / 12. 5. 31				25. 7. 45	1. 7. 40 / 16. 7. 45
94	R-17		Union Iron Works	5. 5. 17	24. 12. 17	17. 8. 18 / 15. 5. 31			9. 3. 42 = RN	22. 6. 45	25. 3. 41 / 9. 3. 42
95	R-18		Union Iron Works	16. 6. 17	8. 1. 18	11. 9. 18 / 13. 5. 31				10. 45	8. 1. 41 / 19. 9. 45
96	R-19		Union Iron Works	23. 6. 17	28. 1. 18	10. 7. 18 / 15. 5. 31	(21. 6. 42)		9. 3. 42 = RN		6. 1. 41 / 9. 3. 42
97	R-20		Union Iron Works	4. 6. 17	21. 1. 18	26. 10. 18 / 15. 5. 31				10. 45	22. 1. 41 / 27. 9. 45

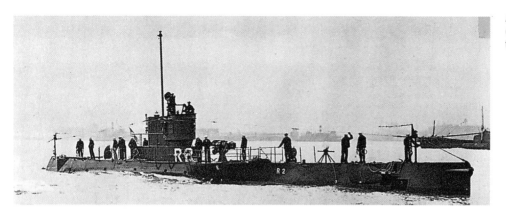

An undated photograph of *R-2* (SS-79); note the 3in gun in front of the conning tower. [USN]

Another undated photograph, this time of *R-10* (SS-87). The use of the white star as an identification mark is, to say the least, unusual. [USN]

Old S Class (SS-105)

At the beginning of the War there were still – or again – 38 S-Class boats that, like those of the two previous classes, had never been given names. It should also be noted that their S-based identification numbers had nothing to do with the official 'SS' designations under which all boats were classified. This large class of boats was divided into four groups, each with slightly greater displacement and a somewhat different appearance. In December 1941 the S Class consisted of:

1st Group *S-1, S-18, S-20* to *S-41*
2nd Group *S-11* to *S-17*
3rd Group *S-42* to *S-47*
4th Group *S-48*

Again as with the previous classes, the S-Class boats were the result of First World War planning, and with them formed the bulk of the American submarine fleet between the wars until the advent of large numbers of the heavier boats of the 1920s and 1930s. The small displacement of these vessels permitted only light armament, and their range was far too short for the Pacific, but otherwise they went through the full gamut of operational possibilities. They carried out coastal duties on the Pacific seaboard of the USA and in the Far East, normal submarine operations within the limitations of their range, training duties for sonar and other applications, and as training partners for destroyers, frigates, corvettes, and submarine chasers. In the course of their 20-year life, some boats had active periods interspersed with periods of inactivity, without being officially decommissioned. Then, in the mid-1930s, conditions became such that they were taken out of service. But again, a mere four to six years later, before the USA entered the War, they were returned to service and remained operational until the end of the War. Within their limitations these boats were extremely valuable. Nevertheless there were losses over this period, three due to military action, and four to other causes. To strengthen the British submarine fleet, six units were transferred to the Royal Navy.

S Class (1st group)

Pennant numbers	Ships in the class		displacement surfaced	Dimensions m			Output HP	Speed kn	Range Sm/kn	Oil fuel ts	Comple- ment	Original combat systems
SS	plan- ned	com- pleted	submerged	length	beam	draught					Officers/ enlisted	
105, 123, 125 – 146	–	24	854	66,9	6,3	4,6	Diesel 1200	14,5		158,7	4/34	1 – 4in L/50 (SS-128, SS-135 to-139, SS-145: 1 – 3in, all 4 bow torpedo tubes 21in (12 Torpedoes)
			1062	Operating depth 61 m			electric motors 1500	11				

S Class (1st group)

Pen- nant num- ber	Name	FY	Building yard	Keel laid	launched	commis- sioned / decom- missioned	war (and other) loss	reclas- sified	transferred to	stricken	Remarks
105	S-1		Bethlehem Quincy	11. 12. 17	26. 10. 18	5. 6. 20 / 20. 10. 37			20. 4. 42 = RN	24. 6. 42	16. 10. 40 / 20. 4. 42
123	S-18		Bethlehem Quincy	15. 8. 18	29. 4. 20	3. 4. 24 / 29. 10. 45				13. 11. 45	
125	S-20		Bethlehem Quincy	15. 8. 18	9. 6. 20	22. 11. 22 / 16. 7. 45				25. 7. 45	
126	S-21		Bethlehem Quincy	19. 12. 18	18. 8. 20	14. 9. 23 / 14. 9. 42			14. 9. 42 = RN		
127	S-22		Bethlehem Quincy	6. 1. 19	15. 7. 20	23. 6. 24 / 19. 6. 42			19. 6. 42 = RN	8. 45	
128	S-23		Bethlehem Quincy	18. 1. 19	27. 10. 20	30. 10. 23 / 2. 11. 45				16. 11. 45	
129	S-24		Bethlehem Quincy	1. 11. 18	27. 6. 22	24. 8. 23 / 10. 8. 42			10. 8. 42 = RN	45	
130	S-25		Bethlehem Quincy	26. 10. 18	29. 5. 22	9. 7. 23 / 4. 11. 41	2. 5. 42		4. 11. 45 = via RN to Poland		
131	S-26		Bethlehem Quincy	7. 11. 19	22. 8. 22	15. 10. 23	24. 1. 42				
132	S-27		Bethlehem Quincy	11. 4. 19	18. 10. 22	22. 1. 24	(19. 6. 42)				
133	S-28		Bethlehem Quincy	16. 4. 19	20. 9. 22	13. 12. 23	(4. 7. 44)				

Pennant number	Name	FY	Building yard	Keel laid	launched	commissioned / decommissioned	war (and other) loss	reclassified	transferred to	stricken	Remarks
134	S-29		Bethlehem Quincy	17. 4. 19	9. 11. 22	22. 5. 24 / 5. 6. 42			5. 6. 42 = RN	46	
135	S-30		Bethlehem S. Franc.	1. 4. 18	21. 11. 18	29. 10. 20 / 9. 10. 45				24. 10. 45	
136	S-31		Bethlehem S. Franc.	13. 4. 18	28. 12. 18	11. 5. 22 / 19. 10. 45				1. 11. 45	
137	S-32		Bethlehem S. Franc.	12. 4. 18	11. 1. 19	15. 6. 22* / 7. 12. 37				1. 11. 45	18. 9. 40* / 19. 10. 45
138	S-33		Bethlehem S. Franc.	14. 6. 18	5. 12. 18	18. 4. 22 / 1. 12. 37*				1. 11. 45	16. 10. 40* / 23. 10. 45
139	S-34		Bethlehem S. Franc.	28. 5. 18	13. 2. 19	12. 7. 22 / 23. 10. 45				11. 45	
140	S-35		Bethlehem S. Franc.	14. 6. 18	27. 2. 19	17. 8. 22 / 19. 3. 45					
141	S-36		Bethlehem S. Franc.	10. 12. 18	3. 6. 19	4. 4. 23	(20. 1. 42)				
142	S-37		Bethlehem S. Franc.	12. 12. 18	20. 6. 19	16. 7. 23 / 6. 2. 45					
143	S-38		Bethlehem S. Franc.	15. 1. 19	17. 6. 19	11. 5. 23 / 14. 12. 44				20. 1. 45	
144	S-39		Bethlehem S. Franc.	14. 1. 19	2. 7. 19	14. 9. 23	(14. 8. 42)				
145	S-40		Bethlehem S. Franc.	5. 3. 19	5. 1. 21	20. 11. 23 / 29. 10. 45				13. 11. 45	
146	S-41		Bethlehem S. Franc.	17. 4. 19	21. 2. 21	15. 1. 24 / 13. 2. 45				25. 2. 46	

An S-Class boat (1st Group), 66.9 metres in length.

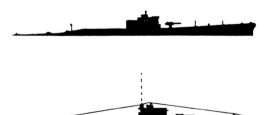

S-20 after rebuild; now 67.7 metres in length.

S-Class (3rd Group)

S Class (2nd group)

Pennant numbers	Ships in the class		displacement surfaced	Dimensions m			Output HP	Speed kn	Range Sm/kn	Oil fuel ts	Comple-ment	Original combat systems
SS	plan-ned	com-pleted	submerged	length	beam	draught					Officers/ enlisted	
116 – 122		7	876	70,5	6,7	4,0	Diesel 2000	15		140	4/34	1 - 4in L/50 SS-109 to -114, -119 to -122: bow torpedo tubes 21in (12 Torpedos, SS-115 to -118, 5 torpedo tubes 21in 4 bow, 1 stern (14 Torpedoes)
			1092	Operating depth 61 m			electric motors 1200	11				

S Class (2nd group)

Pen-nant num-ber	Name	FY	Building yard	Keel laid	launched	commis-sioned decom-missioned	war (and other) loss	reclas-sified	transferred to	stricken	Remarks
116	S-11		Portsmouth NS	2. 12. 19	7. 2. 21	11. 1. 23 / 30. 9. 36				2. 5. 45	6. 9. 40 / 2. 5. 45
117	S-12		Portsmouth NS	8. 1. 20	4. 8. 21	30. 4. 23 / 30. 9. 36				45	4. 11. 40 / 18. 5. 45
118	S-13		Portsmouth NS	14. 2. 20	20. 10. 21	14. 7. 23 / 30. 9. 36				19. 5. 45	28. 10. 40 / 10. 4. 45
119	S-14		Lake Torpedo Boat Co.	7. 12. 17	22. 10. 19	11. 2. 21 / 22. 5. 35				45	10. 12. 40 / 18. 5. 45
120	S-15		Lake Torpedo Boat Co.	13. 12. 17	8. 3. 20	15. 1. 21 / 26. 4. 35				46	3. 1. 41 / 11. 6. 46
121	S-16		Lake Torpedo Boat Co.	19. 3. 18	23. 12. 19	17. 12. 20 / 22. 5. 35				44	2. 12. 40 / 4. 10. 44
122	S-17		Lake Torpedo Boat Co.	19. 3. 18	22. 5. 20	1. 3. 21 / 29. 3. 35				13. 11. 44	16. 12. 40 / 4. 10. 44

S Class (3rd group)

Pennant numbers	Ships in the class		displacement surfaced	Dimensions m			Output HP	Speed kn	Range Sm/kn	Oil fuel ts	Comple-ment	Original combat systems
SS	plan-ned	com-pleted	submerged	length	beam	draught					Officers/enlisted	
153 – 158		6	906	68,7	6,3	4,9	Diesel 1200	14,5		175,5	4/34	1 – 4in L/50
			1126					11				4 bow torpedo
				Operating depth 61m			electric motors 1200					tubes 21in (12 Torpedoes)

S Class (3rd group)

Pen-nant num-ber	Name	FY	Building yard	Keel laid	launched	commis-sioned	war (and other) loss	reclas-sified	transferred to	stricken	Remarks
						decom-missioned					
153	S-42		Bethlehem Quincy	16. 12. 20	30. 4. 23	20. 11. 24				13. 11. 45	
						25. 10. 45					
154	S-43		Bethlehem Quincy	13. 12. 20	31. 3. 23	31. 12. 24				13. 11. 45	
						10. 10. 45					
155	S-44		Bethlehem Quincy	19. 2. 21	27. 10. 23	16. 2. 25	7. 10. 43				
156	S-45		Bethlehem Quincy	29. 12. 20	26. 6. 23	31. 3. 25				13. 11. 45	
						30. 10. 45					
157	S-46		Bethlehem Quincy	23. 2. 21	11. 9. 23	5. 6. 25				13. 11. 45	
						2. 11. 45					
158	S-47		Bethlehem Quincy	26. 2. 21	5. 1. 24	16. 9. 25				13. 11. 45	
						25. 10. 45					

S-30 (SS-135) off the coast of southern California. If the date is accurate, this photograph was taken on 26 August 1920, two months before her official commissioning. [USN]

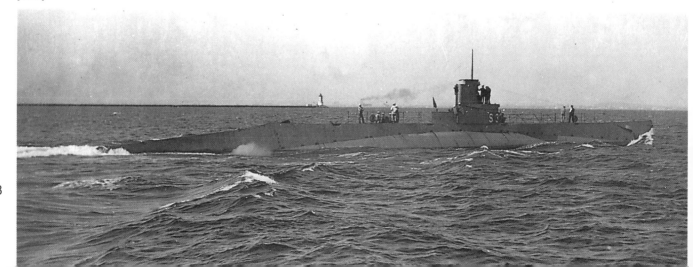

S Class (4th group)

Pennant numbers	Ships in the class		displacement surfaced	Dimensions m			Output HP	Speed kn	Range Sm/kn	Oil fuel ts	Comple-ment	Original combat systems
SS	plan-ned	com-pleted	submerged	length	beam	draught					Officers/enlisted	
159		1	903	73,2	6,4	4,1	Diesel 1800	14,5		168	4/34	1 - 4in L/50 5 torpedo tubes 21in
			1230	Operating depth 61m			electric motors 1500	11				4 bow, 1 stern (14 Torpedoes)

S Class (4th group)

Pen-nant num-ber	Name	FY	Building yard	Keel laid	launched	commis-sioned	war (and other) loss	reclas-sified	transferred to	stricken	Remarks
						decom-missioned					
159	S-48		Lake Torpedo Boat Co.	22. 10. 20	26. 2. 21	14. 10. 22					10. 12. 40
						16. 9. 35					29. 8. 45

This 1938 photograph shows a complete submarine division with the mother ship *Beaver* (AS-5). The boats are *S-30* to *S-35*. [USN]

39

Undated photograph of *S-44* (SS-155); note the 4in gun forward of the conning tower.

Barracuda Class (SS-163)

All the vessels of the previous three classes displaced less than 1,000 tons on the surface. As a result, they possessed neither the range nor the seakeeping characteristics needed for an ocean-going role.

The first attempts to build submarines of more than 1,000 tons were made during the First World War, when, in Fiscal Year 1917, the three T-Class boats displacing 1,106/1,486 tons were constructed. This project outstripped the technology of its time, and the boats rapidly proved unreliable and uneconomic; they were eventually discarded in 1930. As they took no part in the Second World War, no detailed description of them is given in this book.

The advent of the modern 'fleet submarine' came with the introduction of the *Barracuda* Class, which is where the confusion arises regarding nomenclature and the allocation of pennant numbers. It must be borne in mind that the designation 'SS' (for 'submarines') was officially introduced in 1920. The three T-Class boats mentioned above, for example, were never officially allocated the pennant numbers SS-52, SS-60 and SS-61 by which they were later described.

The submarines built from 1924 to 1926 had, instead of names, the numbers *V-1* to *V-3*. Confusingly, they were also designated *SF-4* to *SF-6*, the 'SF' standing for 'Fleet Submarine', and the numbers indicating a sequence beginning with the earlier T-Class boats. They retained this designation for some time, but were finally given the official designations *SS-163* to *SS-165* in 1931. They then became the first boats in the US Navy to be named after sea creatures, all beginning with the letter 'B', which caused them to be referred to as *B-1* to *B-3*, in addition to their official pennant numbers. As a result, these boats, together with some of the following class, had no less than two names and two numbers each! For clarity, this confusing process is summarized in the table below.

Original Designation 1924-6	Name 1924-6	Pennant Number 1931	Name 1931	Additional Name after 1931
SF-4	*V-1*	SS-163	*Barracuda*	B-1
SF-5	*V-2*	SS-164	*Bass*	B-2
SF-6	*V-3*	SS-165	*Bonita*	B-3

At about 2,000 tons surface displacement, these three boats were much more stable than the earlier S-Class boats, which did not count as 'fleet submarines'. It is notable, however, that, contrary to experience in the First World War, the larger boat designs were not used to increase the weight of available armament. So, although the number of torpedo tubes was raised to six from four in the S Class, the complement (twelve) of torpedoes remained the same. In fact, because by this time eyes were turning towards the Pacific, the extra space was used to beef up the powerplant and thus add to the range. For these reasons, too, it was also used to provide improved crew accommodation.

The B-Class boats were immediately recognizable by their sloping deck line and shark-like bows with stem hawsepipe. The higher form of the conning tower was to become a mark of all US submarine classes from then on.

This class was also notable for its powerplant. Surface propulsion was by diesel, supported by auxiliary electric drive. But while the electric drive was always reliable, the diesels regularly caused problems and had to be replaced in 1940. Also, the original 5in armament was replaced with a lighter, 3in, gun in 1928 to improve stability.

By and large, the seaworthiness and general performance of these boats was inadequate, and no one was especially sorry when they were transferred to the Reserve in mid-1937. However, a mere three years later, they were reactivated as US entry into the War became increasingly certain. Deck armament, torpedo tubes and half the powerplant were removed in 1942-3, and the newly available space was used for cargo, although the boats were not reclassified. Their unreliability was further emphasized when, on 17 August 1942, *Bass* had a fire in her after battery room which cost 26 crew members their lives.

From 1940 until their final decommissioning in March 1945, all three boats carried out practice, training and war duties. It is worth noting that conversion to cargo submarines was instigated by President Roosevelt himself. After conversion, these boats were fitted with twin 20mm anti-aircraft cannon as well as SJ and SD radar. With the idea of making use of these unloved boats there arose a plan to convert them to transport submarines, a measure that was eventually suspended. After *Argonaut*, described below, was given the designation APS-1 in September 1942, the three B-Class boats should have been reclassified APS-2 to APS-4, but this did not happen.

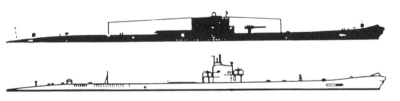

Pre-War silhouette of *Barracuda*.

Wartime silhouette of *Barracuda* Class.

Barracuda Class

Pennant numbers SS	Ships in the class		displacement surfaced submerged	Dimensions m			Output HP	Speed kn	Range Sm/kn	Oil fuel ts	Comple- ment Officers/ enlisted	Original combat systems
	plan- ned	com- pleted		length	beam	draught						
163 – 165	3	3	2000	104,2	8,2	4,4	Diesel-electric. 6200	18,7	10000₁₁	344	orig.: 8/80	1 - 4in L/51, 1928 replaced with
			2620					9	10 Std.₅ endurance 45 days		1931: 7/80	1 - 3in L/50, 1943 removed
			1929: 2119	Operating depth 61 m			electric motors 2400				1938: 7/79	6 torpedo tubes 21in, 4 bow, 2 stern, 12 Torpedoes,
			2506								1943: 9/44	(acc. to other sources, 16) all torpedo tubes removed after 1943

Powerplant: (a) 2 diesels acting on
generator (b) 2 main diesels driving
generator and two electric motors;
directly connected to propeller.

Barracuda Class

Pennant number	Name	FY	Building yard	Keel laid	launched	commis-sioned / decom-missioned	war (and other) loss	reclas-sified	transferred to	stricken	Remarks
163	*Barracuda* (ex-V-1)	21	Portsmouth NS	20. 10. 21	17. 7. 24	1. 10. 24 * 14. 5. 37		APS-2 (intended)		10. 3. 45	5. 9. 40 * 3. 3. 45
164	*Bass* (ex-V-2)	21	Portsmouth NS	20. 10. 21	27. 12. 24	26. 9. 25 * 9. 6. 37		APS-3 (intended)		10. 3. 45	5. 9. 40 * 3. 3. 45
165	*Bonita* (ex-V-3)	21	Portsmouth NS	16. 11. 21	9. 6. 25	22. 5. 26 * 4. 6. 37		APS-4 (intended)		10. 3. 45	5. 9. 40 * 3. 3. 45

A special feature of this class was the sharklike bow, clearly visible here on *Bass* and *Bonita*. Radio masts can be seen above the names. Source and date of photograph unknown.

Undated peacetime photograph of *Bass* (SS-164). Note the boat on deck aft of the conning tower. [USN]

Although already at war (*circa*1943), *Barracuda* still wears pennant number 163. The deck gun is the lighter, 3in, version. [USN]

Undated peacetime photograph of a black-painted *Bonita* (SS-165) sailing under her old number, B-3, and with her name on the bow.

This peacetime (*circa*1938) photograph of *Bonita* was used by the Navy as an identification photograph in 1943. [USN]

Argonaut Class (SS-166)

There was only one boat in this class, planned originally as a minelayer, and she was the only example of this type of submarine in the fleet. As with the previous class, there was confusion over names and pennant numbers, so they are summarized in the following table.

Pennant number 1928	Name 1928	Pennant Number 1931	Name 1931	Additional Name after 1931
SF-7 ab 1931 SM-1	*V-4*	SS-166*	*Argonaut*	A-1

The pennant number SS-166 was never officially allocated.

This was the largest submarine built by the USA in the 1930s, at a cost of $6.15 million. A much larger powerplant was needed, which was where earlier types had failed. She was double-hulled throughout, and was sometimes referred to as a 'submarine cruiser', although the word 'boat' is still used for all submarines, irrespective of size. The design also incorporated a series of structural improvements aimed at achieving a 30m increase in operating depth.

All four torpedo tubes were located in the bows. In the stern were two large rooms for magazines and the relatively complex mine-handling equipment. Mines were laid from two 40in stern launching tubes, and there was a compensation system which adjusted trim as mines were discharged. With this system it was possible to lay eight mines in ten minutes.

From the beginning, the diesels did not produce the power needed for wartime service, but a replacement of the main diesels planned for 1941 was abandoned with the USA's entry into the War. However, from January to July 1942, *Argonaut* was rebuilt, retaining the minelaying gear but finally replacing the inadequate diesels. Two external torpedo tubes were fitted on the afterdeck. Then followed a hasty transformation to troop carrier, with capacity for underwater transport of 120 men and their equipment; the designation was changed to APS-1, and an SJ radar was fitted.

In some ways, this boat resembled the large U-boats of the First World War. She had an imposing armament mounted forward and aft of the conning tower, consisting of two 6in guns of the L/53 type which made her suitable for deployment against merchant shipping. Her slow speed and poor manoeuvrability eventually led to her doom, for she was sunk with the loss of 105 men in action against Japanese destroyers in 1943.

Argonaut's silhouette during the Second World War.

Argonaut Class

Pennant numbers SS	Ships in the class		displacement surfaced submerged	Dimensions m			Output HP	Speed kn	Range Sm/kn	Oil fuel ts	Comple- ment Officers/ enlisted	Original combat systems
	plan- ned	com- pleted		length	beam	draught						
[166]	1	1	3046 4164 1929: 2680 4080	116,2 Operating depth 91 m	10,3	4,7	Diesel-electric 3175 electric motors 2200	15 8	10000_{10} 10 Std.$_5$ endurance 90 days	658	orig.: 8/78 1931: 7/80	2 - 6in L/53 Mk XII, 4 bow torpedo tubes 21in (16 Torpedoes) 60 mines Mk XI (2 minelaying tubes 40in)

Powerplant: (a) 2 diesels acting on generator (b) 2 main diesels driving generator and two electric motors; directly connected to propeller.

Pennant number	Name	FY	Building yard	Keel laid	launched	commissioned / decommissioned	war (and other) loss	reclassified	transferred to	stricken	Remarks
[163]*	*Argonaut* (ex-V-4)	25	Portsmouth NS	1. 5. 25	10. 11. 27	10. 11. 27 / 2. 4. 28	10. 1. 43	9/42 = APS-1			*These pennant numbers were not officially allocated

In this Navy identification photograph dated 18 July 1942, *Argonaut* can be seen bearing the SM-1 designation. She is in wartime black, and there are slight modifications to her conning tower. [USN]

▲
These two peacetime photographs show *Argonaut* with her old V-4 designation. The supposedly official pennant number SS-166 was never actually allocated. Note the light gray paintwork, the mast on the conning tower, and how the hull has been extended to take the mountings for the two 6in guns. [USN]
▼

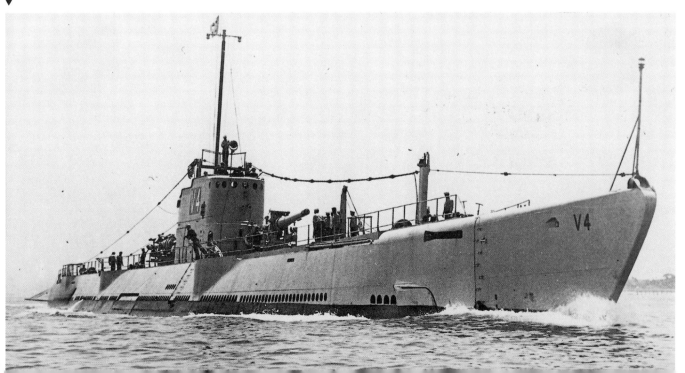

Narwhal Class (SS-167)

Kennung 1930	Name 1930	Baunummer 1931	Name 1931	Additional name after 1931
SF-8 SC-1	V-5	SS-167	Narwhal	N 1
SF-9 SC-2	V-6	SS-168	Nautilus	N 2

Ordered during Fiscal Year 1926, both these boats had a lot in common with *Argonaut*, except that they were conceived and built as submarine cruisers from the outset. A greatly enhanced torpedo complement replaced the minelaying equipment, so that even in the pre-War period a total of 26 torpedoes was carried. Once again, size caused problems; for example they were easy to locate whether surfaced or submerged. On the credit side, they were very roomy, had considerable firepower from their two 6in deck guns, and were able to launch torpedoes astern as well as ahead. There were permanent problems with the diesels, and the design speed of 21 knots was never attained.

After the losses of the earlier *S-51* and *S-4*, greater emphasis was placed on safety in the design of these boats. Provision was made for rescue of the crew and the recovery of the vessel in the event of an accident.

In 1940-1, it was intended to re-engine both boats, but the course of the War dictated otherwise. Shortly after the beginning of the War, *Nautilus* became a submarine tanker, and was used for refuelling long-range reconnaissance flying-boats. In mid-1941, during a routine refit, it was decided to increase her combat effectiveness, so she was finally given much-needed new diesels, and fitted with radar and an underwater fire-control system. Four additional deck torpedo tubes were installed, but they were not entirely successful and had to be repositioned in 1943. The modernization of *Narwhal* was delayed for about a year, and so she too received improved diesels.

Although their armament was now sufficient to make effective fighting units, these boats were still employed in areas where their carrying capacity was useful. In 1942-3 temporary modifications were carried out which enabled them to be used as troop carriers with space for 120 Marines, although they were not reclassified APS. They had more luck than the unfortunate *Argonaut* and carried out many successful transport missions, a role which had never been planned for them when they were first designed.

Narwhal Class

Pennant numbers SS	Ships in the class planned	Ships in the class completed	displacement surfaced submerged	Dimensions m length	beam	draught	Output HP	Speed kn	Range Sm/kn	Oil fuel ts	Complement Officers/ enlisted	Original combat systems
167, 168	2	2	SS-167 1943: 3128 / 4023 / SS-168 1942: 3158 / 4040 / Operating depth 91 m	113,0	10,1		Diesel-electric 5600 / 1600	17,4 / 8	18 000$_{10}$ / 10 Std.$_5$ endurance 90 days	692 SS-168 1942: 558 to Diesel +69 to gasoline	1931: 9/80 1942: 9/88 1943: 8/80	2 - 6in L/53 Mk XII, 6 torpedo tubes 21in, 4 bow, 2 stern 1942/43 4 additional torpedo tubes on deck 21in (1942: internal: max. 26, external: max, 16 = 42 Torpedoes)

Anordnung Antriebsanlage: a) 2 Diesel wirken auf Generator. – b) 2 Haupt-Diesel treiben Generator und 2 E-Motoren an; auf Propeller geschaltet.

Narwhal Class

Pennant number	Name	FY	Building yard	Keel laid	launched	commissioned decommissioned	war (and other) loss	reclassified	transferred to	stricken	Remarks
167	Narwhal (ex-V-5)	26	Portsmouth NS	10. 5. 27	17. 12. 28	15. 5. 30 / 23. 4. 45				19. 5. 45	1942–45 cargo submarine
168	Nautilus (ex-V-6)	26	Mare Island NS	2. 8. 27	15. 3. 30	1. 7. 30 / 30. 6. 45				25. 7. 45	1942–54 cargo submarine

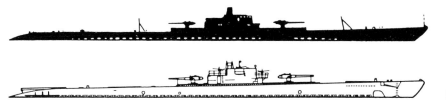

Pre-war silhouette of Narwhal.

Wartime silhouette of Narwhal.

◀
Peacetime photograph of Narwhal (SS-167) bearing the old V-5 designation. [USN]

Navy identification photograph taken off Mare Island on 15 April 1942 of Nautilus (SS-168) in black. The twin 6in deck guns give an impression of great power, and the forward external torpedo tube can easily be seen. [USN]
▼

Dolphin Class (SS-169)

Designation 1930	Name before 1932	Pennant number 1932	Name 1932	Additional pennant number after 1932
SF-10 SC-3	*V-7*	SS-169	*Dolphin*	D-1

Because the first six V-boats had not been exactly successful – partly because of their size but also the inadequacy of their diesels – the Navy decided to try a new approach. The result of their deliberations was this single boat, *SF-10*, the name of which was changed from *V-7* to *Dolphin* during building. The object of this totally new development was to cram the design intentions of the earlier V Classes into a hull only half their size. This meant, *inter alia*, a radically new hull layout, which meant relocating major components such as the fuel tanks. The reduction in interior space also meant that only eighteen torpedoes could be carried, and so, in 1933, it was found possible to carry a further three as deck cargo in the low bulge aft of the conning tower. A small loading boom was also fitted. The previous V-Class boats had three periscopes; *Dolphin* had only two. The powerplant was the same as that of the

Narwhal Class; with these MAN diesels, it proved possible to reach the design speed of 17 knots – although of course this was partly due to the fact that she was only half the size. However, the MAN diesels lasted *Dolphin* for the whole of her service life.

During 1942 *Dolphin* undertook three missions in the Pacific, between each of which periods of repair were needed. In fact she needed a thorough modernization, but her general condition was so poor that, in view of the demand for yard space to build new submarines and other, more important, ships, no berth could be made available. In 1943, therefore, *Dolphin* was transferred to training duties for new crews at Pearl Harbor and New London, with her operating depth reduced on safety grounds to 46 metres.

In general, *Dolphin* was not a very successful design. This was mainly because the technology of the early 1930s was not up to building medium-sized submarines without significant loss of fighting capability. This showed up particularly in limited range and a light structure which, with a safety factor of only 1.5, imposed severe restrictions on operating depth. As the photographs show, in terms of appearance, *Dolphin* had little in common with her larger predecessors, except perhaps to serve as a prototype for classes built during the later years of the thirties.

Pre-War silhouette of *Dolphin*.

Dolphin Class

Pennant numbers SS	Ships in the class		displacement surfaced submerged	Dimensions m			Output HP	Speed kn	Range Sm/kn	Oil fuel ts	Complement Officers/ enlisted	Original combat systems
	planned	completed		length	beam	draught						
169	1	1	Orig.: 1718	97,4	8,5	4,05	Diesel-electric 4086	17	6 000$_{10}$	390	1938: 7/56	1 - 4in L/50 4 bow, 2 stern torpedo tubes 21in (18 Torpedos internal, 3 external)
								8	16 000$_7$		1945: 7/70	
			2240 später: 1560	Operating depth 106 m			electric motors 1750		10 Std.$_5$ 75 days endurance			
			2215									

Powerplant: (a) 2 diesels acting on generator (b) 2 main diesels driving generator and two electric motors; directly connected to propeller.

Pennant number	Name	FY	Building yard	Keel laid	launched	commissioned / decommissioned	war (and other) loss	reclassified	transferred to	stricken	Remarks
169	Dolphin (ex-V-7)	30	Portsmouth NS	14. 6. 30	8. 3. 32	1. 6. 32 / 2. 10. 45				24. 10. 45	

Dolphin (SS-169) in an undated peacetime photograph with the designation D-1, showing a gunnery exercise with the 4in gun. Note the torpedo loading booms forward and aft.

Cachalot Class (SS-170)

Designation 1933	Additional name 1933	Pennant number 1933	Name 1933	Additional pennant number after 1933
SF-11 SC-4	V-8	SS-170	Cachalot	C-1
SF-12 SC-5	V-9	SS-171	Cuttlefish	C-2

The last two units of the nine which made up the V-group were the least important. The aim was to achieve a displacement rather smaller than that of Dolphin and in this the designers were successful: both Cachalot and Cuttlefish ended up lighter than intended. There were two reasons for this. The first was a new diesel engine imported from Germany; with only two of these it was possible to reach the same power output as four of the older type of engine had produced in Dolphin. The second reason lay in the fact that the Electric Boat shipyard for the first time made extensive use of welding technology in the hull and fuel tanks. In contrast, the Portsmouth Naval Yard still riveted their boats. However, while these two boats were more successful than Dolphin, they were not successful enough for the Pacific, where ranges of 12,000 nautical miles were required. Furthermore, the new direct-drive diesels, originally so successful, proved unusable because of excessive vibration. They were fairly quickly replaced with GM diesels, but these had to drive through reduction gearing, which was not very practicable for submarine use. But there were two notable firsts with this class: the introduction of an analog computer for torpedo fire control, and, in Cuttlefish, the installation of a prototype air-conditioning system.

Given their limited range and speed, however, these boats were not really successful. Furthermore, they

49

could only mount a 3in deck gun, originally located aft of the conning tower, but later moved forward, where it presumably helped keep the foreship lower in the water. Among the wartime modifications was the removal of the conning-tower fairings in order to fit a platform for 20mm AA cannon. Wartime conning tower modifications can be seen on all boats, especially those of the older classes. After three patrols, both boats were transferred to training duties at New London where, because of their more modern technology, they proved more useful than the old O- and R-Class boats.

Cachalot Class

Pennant numbers SS	Ships in the class		displacement surfaced submerged	Dimensions m			Output HP	Speed kn	Range Sm/kn	Oil fuel ts	Comple-ment Officers/ enlisted	Original combat systems
	plan-ned	com-pleted		length	beam	draught						
170, 171	2	2	1130	170: 82,9	7,3	3,9	Diesel-electric 3070	16,5	$11\,000_{10}$	315	1938: 6/39 1945: 7/48	1 - 3in L/50 4 bow, 2 stern torpedo tubes 21in (16 Torpedos)
			1650	171: 83,6	7,6	3,9	electric motors 1600	8	10 Std.$_5$ 75 days endurance			
				Operating depth 76 m								

Powerplant: (a) 2 main and 1 auxiliary diesel driving generator and 2 electric motors.

Cachalot Class

Pen-nant num-ber	Name	FY	Building yard	Keel laid	launched	commis-sioned decom-missioned	war (and other) loss	reclas-sified	transferred to	stricken	Remarks
170	Cachalot (ex-V-8)	32	Portsmouth NS	21. 10. 31	19. 10. 33	1. 12. 33 17. 10. 45				1) 1. 11. 45 2) 3. 7. 46	*28.11.45 * transferred to NVR
171	Cuttlefish (ex-V-9)	32	Electric Boat	7. 10. 31	21. 11. 33	8. 6. 34 24. 10. 45				3. 7. 46	

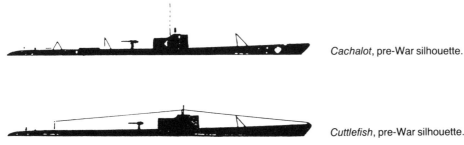

Cachalot, pre-War silhouette.

Cuttlefish, pre-War silhouette.

Undated photograph of *Cachalot*, already in wartime black and carrying the designation SS-170. [USN]

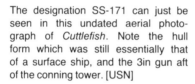

The designation SS-171 can just be seen in this undated aerial photograph of *Cuttlefish*. Note the hull form which was still essentially that of a surface ship, and the 3in gun aft of the conning tower. [USN]

P Class (1st Group) (SS-172)

The ten boats that made up the P Class consisted of three groups with slightly different characteristics. They were quite unlike the V-boats, and were built under their allocated SS numbers and given names. They also had the peacetime designations P-1 to P-10, as shown in the A-Tables. The two boats that made up the First Group were built by the Navy itself; their design was the result of sensible compromises between the over-heavy V-boats and the lightweight *Cachalot* Class. This design also included the first trials of full diesel-electric drive; in other words, the diesel was no longer directly coupled to the propeller, but to a generator which powered electric motors to drive the propeller. There were a few teething troubles at first, but these were overcome by replacing the diesels as the War progressed. This had an effect on space requirements in that a larger engine room was needed. They were still fully riveted boats, and they followed the trend of the times by having two additional deck-mounted torpedo tubes.

Up until the autumn of 1942, both boats carried out several patrols in the Pacific. Then, because of supply problems and the arrival of more modern units, they were transferred to the training base at New London, where they gave valuable service as training boats until the end of the War. After being discarded in November 1945, both boats served as stationary training hulks until 1956.

These were almost the last double-hulled submarines. They were the first to have had air-conditioning fitted as standard which, as well as ensuring the wellbeing of the crew, helped to ensure trouble-free running of the electric powerplant.

P Class (2nd Group) (SS-174)

Shark and *Tarpon* were two names outside the run of the P Class, but, as they were clearly P-Class boats, they were given the designations *P-3* and *P-4*. Armament and powerplant were similar to the First Group, 51 but, in contrast to *P-1* and *P-2*, these two were single hulled, though they did share the same engine troubles. They were built by Electric Boat, a shipyard that produced the first fully welded submarines in the US Navy. The advantages of this method of construction were clear: the interior layout of the P-Class boats served as a model for all subsequent wartime submarine classes. *Shark* was lost early in the War, but *Tarpon* survived to have deck-mounted torpedo tubes fitted in 1942, and ended up as a training hulk from 1947 to 1956.

P Class (3rd Group) (SS-176)

The Third Group of the P class was made up of six boats ordered in Fiscal Year 1935. Although there were no noticeable differences in design between these boats and those of the Second Group (in fact the engine room was some 60cm longer), there were considerable differences in building methods. Three different yards were involved in the construction of P-5 to P-10. The Navy had become convinced of the advantages of the all-welded construction used by Electric Boat, and required the Portsmouth and Mare Island yards to convert to it. However, the latter was unable to do so at the time, with the result that *P-8*, *P-9* and *P-10* were the last submarines in the US Navy to have all-riveted construction.

Different diesels were installed depending on the building yard, but all, notably *P-10*'s, gave the same sort of problems that had been encountered in earlier designs. Three boats of this group were lost in 1942-3, but the others were re-engined and completed up to twelve wartime missions before being discarded. Further to their function as training boats, *P-7* and *P-8* remained in service as training hulks until 1954-6.

Apart from the continuing engine problems, the design of the P-Class boats pointed the way to the later design of the three wartime classes. Moreover, they proved to be the first substantial series after years of trial and error. Four of the ten boats were lost in action.

Class leader *Porpoise* (SS-172) of the First Group, bearing her *P-1* designation. [USN]

Porpoise (P-1-) Class

Pennant numbers SS	Ships in the class		displacement surfaced submerged	Dimensions m			Output HP	Speed kn	Range Sm/kn	Oil fuel ts	Complement Officers/ enlisted	Original combat systems
	planned	completed		length	beam	draught						
172, 173	2	2	1310	91,8	7,6	4,0	Diesel-electric 4300	19	$11\,000_{10}$	1944: 340	1944: 5/45	1 - 3in L/50 4 bow, 2 stern torpedo tubes 21in, 1942: 2 additional deck torpedo tubes (16, from 1942 18 Torpedos)
			1934	Operating depth 76 m			electric motors 2850	8	$10\,\text{Std.}_5$ 75 days endurance			

Powerplant: (a) 4 main and 2 auxiliary diesels operating 2 generators; (b) 4 electric motors driving propeller through reduction gearing.

Porpoise Class, pre-War silhouette.

P Class (1st group)

Pennant number	Name	FY	Building yard	Keel laid	launched	commissioned / decommissioned	war (and other) loss	reclassified	transferred to	stricken	Remarks
172	Porpoise (P-1)	34	Portsmouth NS	27. 10. 33	20. 6. 35	15. 8. 35 * / 15. 11. 45				13. 8. 56	*8.5.47 from 2.56 training hulk
173	Pike (P-2)	34	Portsmouth NS	20. 12. 33	12. 9. 35	2. 12. 35 * / 15. 11. 45				17. 2. 56	*31.7.47 from 17.2.56 training hulk

Shark Class, wartime silhouette.

Shark (P-3) Class

Pennant numbers SS	Ships in the class — planned	Ships in the class — completed	displacement surfaced / submerged	Dimensions m — length	beam	draught	Output HP	Speed kn	Range Sm/kn	Oil fuel ts	Complement Officers/enlisted	Original combat systems
174, 175	2	2	1316 / 1968	90,9	7,7	4,3	4300 / 2085	18 / 8	11000_{10} / 10 Std.$_5$ 75 days endurance	328	5/45	1 - 3in L/50 4 bow, 2 stern torpedo tubes 21in SS-175 1942: 2 additional deck torpedo tubes (16 to 18 Torpedos)

Operating depth 76 m

Powerplant: (a) 4 main and 2 auxiliary diesels operating 2 generators; (b) 4 electric motors driving propeller through reduction gearing.

Perch Class, pre-War silhouette.

Perch (P-5) Class

Pennant numbers	Ships in the class		displacement surfaced	Dimensions m			Output HP	Speed kn	Range Sm/kn	Oil fuel ts	Comple-ment	Original combat systems
SS	plan-ned	com-pleted	submerged	length	beam	draught					Officers/ enlisted	
176 – 181	6	6	1515	91,7	7,7	4,2	Diesel-electric 4300	18,8	$11\,000_{10}$	351	5/45, 1945: 8/65	1 - 3in L/50 4 bow, 2 stern torpedo tubes 21in SS-177, -178, 1942/43 2 additional deck torpedo tubes (16 to 18 Torpedos)
			1997	Operating depth 76 m				8	$10\,\text{Std.}_5$ 75 days endurance			
			1945:				2285 (varying depending on engine type)					
			2020									

Powerplant SS-176 – SS-178: (a) 4 main and 2 auxiliary diesels operating 2 generators; (b) 8 electric motors driving propeller through reduction gearing; SS-179 – SS-181: as before, but with 4 electric motors.

Pickerel, bearing her 'SS' designation 177. [AB]

One of the Third Group of the P Class, *Perch* (SS-176), in wartime black. [USN]

P Class (2nd group)

Pen-nant num-ber	Name	FY	Building yard	Keel laid	launched	commis-sioned / decom-missioned	war (and other) loss	reclas-sified	transferred to	stricken	Remarks
174	*Shark* (P-3)	34	Electric Boat	24. 10. 33	21. 5. 35	25. 1. 36	~ 11. 2. 42				
175	*Tarpon* (P-4)	34	Electric Boat	22. 12. 33	4. 9. 35	12. 3. 36 / 15. 11. 45	(26. 8. 57)			5. 9. 56	*17.4.47 to 5.9.56 training hulk

P Class (3rd group)

Pen-nant num-ber	Name	FY	Building yard	Keel laid	launched	commis-sioned / decom-missioned	war (and other) loss	reclas-sified	transferred to	stricken	Remarks
176	*Perch* (P-5)	35	Electric Boat	25. 2. 35	9. 5. 36	19. 11. 36	3. 3. 42				
177	*Pickerel* (P-6)	35	Electric Boat	25. 3. 35	7. 7. 36	26. 1. 37	~ 3. 4. 43				
178	*Permit* (ex-Pinna) (P-7)	35	Electric Boat	6. 6. 35	5. 10. 36	17. 3. 37 / 15. 11. 45				26. 7. 56	*24.1.47 to 26.7.56 NRT
179	*Plunger* (P-8)	35	Portsmouth NS	17. 7. 35	8. 7. 36	19. 11. 36 / 15. 11. 45					*5.46 to 2.54 NRT
180	*Pollack* (P-9)	35	Portsmouth NS	1. 10. 35	15. 9. 36	15. 1. 37 / 21. 9. 45				1) 11. 10. 45 2) 29. 10. 46	*28.11.45 transferred to reserve
181	*Pompano* (P-10)	35	Mare Island NS	14. 1. 36	11. 3. 37	12. 6. 37	9. 43				

New S Class (1st Group) (SS-182)

Basically, these boats were slightly enlarged P-Class submarines with two additional stern tubes, necessitating a wider hull. There were also changes in the hybrid powerplant, in that only one diesel was coupled to each pair of electric motors, while the other two drove the generator in the usual way. Some of these engines worked perfectly well; others gave enormous problems and had to be replaced during the course of the War. Bunker and engine room locations also differed from the P-Class boats. Building plans were obviously prepared separately by each yard, since the outline of the conning tower of Electric Boat designs was noticeably different from those of the Portsmouth Navy Yard.

The limits of operational depth were plumbed by *Salmon* which, under intensive depth-charging by the Japanese, dived to more than 150 metres, later surfacing and, despite hull damage, engaging her assailant with deck armament. Most S-boats carried out up to fifteen wartime missions.

The S-designations given in the A Tables were borne by these boats up to the beginning of 1939, after which they carried their 'SS' numbers on the bows and conning tower. At the beginning of the War these too were removed, only to reappear after the War ended.

With sixteen patrols in enemy waters, *Stingray* (SS-186) had the longest operational career of any wartime US submarine. As with others of the class, she had had two additional forward surface torpedo tubes installed in the autumn of 1942, but these were removed in 1943.

New S Class (2nd Group) (SS-188)

Four boats of this group were lost during the War, which was not exactly encouraging for the crews of the remaining boats, especially since *Squalus* (SS-192) had sunk in May 1939 when her main induction valve failed to close, with the loss of 23 men. Four months later she was refloated, refitted and returned to service renamed *Sailfish* but retaining the number '192', under which designation she survived the War.

There was little difference between these boats and those of the First Group. Some small changes were made in the layout of the fuel tanks, and the hull was some 60cm longer to give better access to the after engine room. There were also some slight differences in the appearance of the conning tower. The last four units reverted to the normal diesel-electric powerplant. A considerable advance on the P Class was a doubling of the battery capacity, giving these boats much greater underwater endurance.

Sealion (SS-195) was the first US submarine to be lost in the Second World War. Having survived only one patrol, she was hit by a Japanese bomb while undergoing repairs at Cavite in the Philippines, and was scuttled on Christmas Day, 1941 to prevent her falling into enemy hands.

It is worth noting that the equivalent Japanese submarines of the time were 3 knots faster on the surface, and had ranges 5,000nm greater, although with some loss of firepower (14 torpedoes, 6 tubes).

Salmon Class, pre-War silhouette.

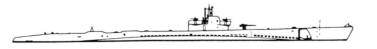

Salmon Class, wartime silhouette

Salmon (S-1) Class

Pennant numbers SS	Ships in the class		displacement surfaced submerged	Dimensions m			Output HP	Speed kn	Range Sm/kn	Oil fuel ts	Comple- ment Officers/ enlisted	Original combat systems
	planned	com- pleted		length	beam	draught						
182 – 187	6	6	1670 2210	93,9	8,0	4,4	5500 2660	21 9	11000_{10} 48 Std.$_2$ 75 days endurance 75 Tage	363	5/50 1945: 10/65	1 - 3in L/50 or 1 - 4in L/50 4 bow, 4 stern torpedo tubes 21in (20 Torpedoes, or 2 mines in place of 1 torpedo up to max 32)
			Operating depth 76 m									

Powerplant: Hybrid (a) 2 main and 2 auxiliary diesels operating gener- ator; (b) 2 main diesels and 4 electric motors driving propeller through reduction gearing.

Stingray (SS-186) photographed off Mare Island, 2 October 1942. A bow- mounted surface torpedo tube is visible, and there is a 3in gun mounted astern of the conning tower. [USN]

New S Class (1st group)

Pen- nant num- ber	Name	FY	Building yard	Keel laid	launched	commis- sioned decom- missioned	war (and other) loss	reclas- sified	transferred to	stricken	Remarks
182	Salmon (S-1)	36	Electric Boat	15. 4. 36	12. 6. 37	15. 3. 38 24. 9. 45				11. 10. 45	
183	Seal (S-2)	36	Electric Boat	25. 5. 36	25. 8. 37	30. 4. 38 15. 11. 45				1. 5. 56	*19.6.47 to 1956 NRT
184	Skipjack (S-3)	36	Electric Boat	22. 7. 36	23. 10. 37	30. 6. 38 28. 8. 46	(25. 7. 46) Bikini; raised 11.8.48			13. 9. 48	
185	Snapper (S-4)	36	Portsmouth NS	23. 7. 36	24. 8. 37	15. 12. 37 15. 11. 45				30. 4. 48	
186	Stingray (S-5)	36	Portsmouth NS	1. 10. 36	6. 10. 37	15. 3. 38 17. 10. 45				1) 1. 11. 45 2) 3. 7. 46	*28.11.45 later in NVR
187	Sturgeon (S-6)	36	Mare Island NS	27. 10. 36	15. 3. 38	25. 6. 38 15. 11. 45				30. 4. 48	

Salmon (SS-182), lead ship of her group, seen in 1940. [USN]

Peacetime photograph of *Seal* (SS-183), First Group. [AB]

Off to war! *Stingray* (SS-186), with lower conning tower, 20mm anti-aircraft guns on both cigarette decks, and 3in gun relocated forward, January 1944. [USN] ▼

Sturgeon (SS-187), with original conning tower. [AB]

Sargo (S-7)-Class

Pennant numbers SS	Ships in the class		displacement surfaced submerged	Dimensions m			Output HP	Speed kn	Range Sm/kn	Oil fuel ts	Comple- ment Officers/ enlisted	Original combat systems
	plan- ned	com- pleted		length	beam	draught						
188 – 197	10	10	1900	94,7	8,3	4,2	5500	20	$11\,000_{10}$	412	5/50 1945: 10/68	1 - 3in L/50 or 1 - 4in L/50 4 bow, 4 stern-torpedo tubes 21in (20 Torpedoes, or 2 mines in place of 1 torpedo up to max 32)
			2350	Operating depth 76 m			2740	9	48 Std.$_2$ endurance 75 days			

Powerplant: *SS-188* to *SS-193* hybrid plan: (a) 2 main and 2 auxiliary diesels operating generator (b) 2 main diesels and 4 electric motors driving propeller through reduction gearing. *SS-194* to *SS-197*: (a) 4 main and 2 auxiliary diesels operating 2 generators; (b) 4 electric motors driving propeller through reduction gearing.

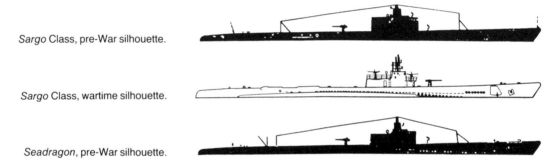

Sargo Class, pre-War silhouette.

Sargo Class, wartime silhouette.

Seadragon, pre-War silhouette.

Sargo (SS-188), lead ship of the Second Group of the S Class, with additional conning tower fairing and 3in gun. [AB]

Much later (August 1944), *Sargo* appears with stripped conning tower, and the heavier 4in gun mounted on the after deck. [USN] ▼

New S Class (2nd group)

Pennant number	Name	FY	Building yard	Keel laid	launched	commissioned / decommissioned	war (and other) loss	reclassified	transferred to	stricken	Remarks
188	Sargo (S-7)	37	Electric Boat	12. 5. 37	6. 6. 38	7. 2. 39 / 22. 6. 46				19. 7. 46	
189	Saury (S-8)	37	Electric Boat	28. 6. 37	20. 8. 38	3. 4. 39 / 22. 6. 46				19. 7. 46	
190	Spearfish (S-9)	37	Electric Boat	9. 9. 37	29. 10. 38	19. 7. 39 / 22. 6. 46				19. 7. 46	
191	Sculpin (S-10)	37	Portsmouth NS	7. 9. 37	27. 7. 38	16. 1. 39	19. 11. 43				
192	Squalus* (S-11)	37	Portsmouth NS	18. 10. 37	14. 9. 38	1. 3. 39 / 15. 11. 39	(23.5.39) raised 9/39				*renamed Sailfish after rebuilding
192	Sailfish ex-Squalus	37				15. 5. 40 / 27. 10. 45				30. 4. 48	
193	Swordfish* (S-12)	37	Mare Island NS	27. 10. 37	1. 4. 39	22. 7. 39	~ 12. 1. 45				
194	Seadragon (S-13)	38	Electric Boat	18. 4. 38	11. 4. 39	23. 10. 39 / 15. 11. 45				30. 4. 48	
195	Sealion (S-14)	38	Electric Boat	20. 6. 38	25. 5. 39	27. 11. 39	25. 12. 41				
196	Searaven (S-15)	38	Portsmouth NS	9. 8. 38	21. 6. 39	2. 10. 39 / 11. 12. 46	(11. 9. 48) Bikini			21. 10. 48	
197	Seawolf (S-16)	38	Portsmouth NS	27. 9. 38	15. 8. 39	1. 12. 39	3. 10. 44				

Peacetime photograph of *Saury* (SS-189) with aft-mounted 3in gun. [AB]

Spearfish (SS-190) with stripped-down conning tower and 3in gun forward. This photograph was probably taken off Point Loma in the Bay of San Diego in May 1943. [USN]

Close-up of midship section of Sculpin (SS-191), lost in 1943. [AB]

Recommissioning of the former Squalus, recovered after a diving accident and renamed Sailfish (SS-192), 15 May 1940. [USN]

This photograph of Sailfish was taken off the Californian coast during the War. The 3in gun is now mounted forward and, unusually, the 20mm anti-aircraft guns are fitted with a shield. [USN]

Swordfish (SS-193), lost at the beginning of 1945. [AB]

Since Atlantic submarines sometimes wore their pennant numbers in wartime, it is impossible to date this photograph of *Seadragon* (SS-194). [AB]

Sealion (SS-195) survived for only two years before being lost (Christmas 1941), which means that this photograph must date from 1940-1. [AB)]

Searaven (SS-196) in wartime rig, May 1943: stripped-down conning tower, 3in gun forward, and mounts for 20mm AA guns on both cigarette decks. In this case the AA gun barrels were stored dry. [USN]   ▼

T Class (SS-198)

With the introduction of this class, the Navy attained what they felt was the standard required in peacetime. Not only did these boats (the last of the fleet submarines to go into service during 1940-1, just before the USA entered the War) set standards for the mass-produced submarines of the three wartime classes, but they strongly resembled them in outward appearance.

This class was actually known as the T Class and the first six boats carried the numbers T-1 to T-6, but, as with the S-groups, this was before launching; during the few remaining months of peace, they carried their official 'SS' number on the bows and conning tower, before having them removed entirely with the onset of war. The second set of six boats, built during 1940, were given names beginning with G, but they were still part of the T (or *Tambor*) Class.

The T-boats were a direct development of the previous S-Class boats. The conning tower was somewhat longer, but the main feature was the inclusion, at the urging of serving submarine officers, of two extra bow torpedo tubes. Although this brought the number of tubes up to ten, it was still only possible to carry fourteen reloads. Also, since many boats were fitted with the heavy 5in L/51 surface-fire gun, wider and stronger mounting points had to be provided.

There are conflicting claims regarding powerplant: H T Lenton states that this class went back to direct diesel-electric drive, but Alden says that reduction gearing was used. The twelve T-boats carried out numerous wartime missions, and no less than seven were lost.

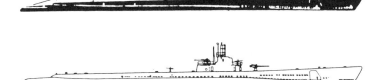

Tambor Class, pre-War silhouette.

Tambor Class, wartime silhouette.

Tambor Class

Pennant numbers SS	Ships in the class		displacement surfaced submerged	Dimensions m			Output HP	Speed kn	Range Sm/kn	Oil fuel ts	Comple-ment Officers/ enlisted	Original combat systems
	plan-ned	com-pleted		length	beam	draught						
198 – 203 206 – 211	12	12	1475 Standard 2370	93,7	8,3	4,2	Diesel-electric 5400 electric motors 2740	20 9	$11\,000_{10}$ 48 Std.$_2$ endurance 75 days	365	6/54 1945: 10/69	1 - 3in L/50 or 1 - 5in L/51 6 bow, 4 stern torpedo tubes 21in (24 Torpedos, or 2 mines in place of 1 torpedo up to max 40)
			Operating depth 76 m									

Powerplant: (a) 4 main and 2 auxiliary diesels operating 2 generators; (b) 4 electric motors driving the propeller through reduction gearing.

Pennant number	Name	FY	Building yard	Keel laid	launched	commissioned / decommissioned	war (and other) loss	reclassified	transferred to	stricken	Remarks
198	*Tambor*	39	Electric Boat	16. 1. 39	20. 12. 39	3. 6. 40 / 10. 12. 45				1. 9. 59	*2. 4. 47 / 1. 9. 59 NRT
199	*Tautog*	39	Electric Boat	1. 3. 39	27. 1. 40	3. 7. 40 / 8. 12. 45				1. 9. 59	*4. 47 / 1. 9. 59 NRT
200	*Thresher*	39	Electric Boat	27. 4. 39	27. 3. 40	27. 8. 40 / 13. 12. 45				23. 12. 47	*6. 2. 46 / 12. 7. 46
201	*Triton*	39	Portsmouth NS	5. 7. 39	25. 3. 40	15. 8. 40	15. 3. 43				
202	*Trout*	39	Portsmouth NS	8. 8. 39	21. 5. 40	15. 11. 40	29. 2. 44				
203	*Tuna*	39	Mare Island NS	19. 7. 39	2. 10. 40	2. 1. 41 / 11. 12. 46	(24. 9. 48) Bikini			21. 10. 48	
206	*Gar*	40	Electric Boat	27. 12. 39	7. 11. 40	14. 4. 41 / 11. 12. 45				1. 8. 59	*4. 47 / 1. 8. 59 NRT
207	*Grampus*	40	Electric Boat	14. 2. 40	23. 12. 40	23. 5. 41	~ 5. 3. 43				
208	*Grayback*	40	Electric Boat	3. 4. 40	31. 1. 41	30. 6. 41	27. 2. 44				
209	*Grayling*	40	Portsmouth NS	15. 12. 39	4. 9. 40	1. 3. 41	~ 12. 9. 43				
210	*Grenadier*	40	Portsmouth NS	2. 4. 40	29. 11. 40	1. 5. 41	21. 4. 43				
211	*Gudgeon*	40	Mare Island NS	22. 11. 39	25. 1. 41	21. 4. 41	~ 18. 4. 44				

Tambor (SS-198), off the coast of Massachusetts, April 1940. This, and the following photographs, show how closely the boats of this class resembled the lead boat. The older, high-mounted type of 3in gun is typical. [AB]

Tautog (SS-199). [AB]

Thresher (SS-200). [AB]

Tuna (SS-203). [AB]

Gar (SS-206). [AB]

Grayling (SS-209), November 1941.
[USN]

Gudgeon (SS-211). [AB]

Grayback (SS-208), 6 May 1941.
[USN]

Mackerel Class (SS-204)

It is difficult to understand why, in 1940, the fleet submarine building programme should have been interrupted to produce two small coastal submarines to designs completely unsuitable for long-range use. It was certainly not the wish of submarine officers to have the *Tambor* Class held up in this way, especially as there was still a good number of the old S-boats which were not up to the demands of the Pacific. Norman Freidman thinks it was simply because Admiral Thomas C. Hart was worried that the fleet submarines were still too big; supposedly, he wanted to replace the old S-boats with this class. Whatever the reasoning, it aroused strong opposition among submarine officers. In the end only two units were built, and even they were quite different from each other, having been built at two different yards.

In general, the Navy was satisfied with the performance of these boats, but they were used mainly as training boats during the War, and saw no war service at all. For surface operation, *Mackerel* had direct-drive diesels, whereas *Marlin* was diesel-electric. During the War, both boats were given machine-guns.

Although the M-Class boats appeared to be small versions of the fleet submarines, they had none of their qualities. However, the design underwent a remarkable resurrection more than fifteen years after they were launched. In the mid-1950s the Peruvian Navy built a group of six boats based on the M-Class, but with their conning towers more like the then current US GUPPY models.

Mackerel Class

Pennant numbers SS	Ships in the class planned	Ships in the class completed	displacement surfaced submerged	Dimensions m length	Dimensions m beam	Dimensions m draught	Output HP	Speed kn	Range Sm/kn	Oil fuel ts	Complement Officers/ enlisted	Original combat systems
204, 205	2	2	204: 835 1190 205: 800 1165	204: 74,2 205: 72,9 Operating depth 76 m	6,8 6,6	3,6 3,6	204: 3360 1500 205: 3400 1500	16 9		88	4/34	1 - 3in L/50 4 bow, 2 stern torpedo tubes 21in (12 Torpedoes)

M Class

Pennant number	Name	FY	Building yard	Keel laid	launched	commissioned decommissioned	war (and other) loss	reclassified	transferred to	stricken	Remarks
204	*Mackerel*	40	Electric Boat	6. 10. 39	28. 9. 40	31. 3. 41 9. 11. 45				28. 11. 45	
205	*Marlin*	40	Portsmouth NS	23. 5. 40	29. 1. 41	1. 8. 41 9. 11. 45				45	

Mackerel Class, pre-War silhouette.

Mackerel (SS-204), one of the two little 'pseudo-fleet submarines'. [AB]

1942-5: THE THREE WARTIME CLASSES

In this section I shall attempt to explain the various circumstances under which the three wartime classes came into existence. It should be remembered that during this period there were other priorities both in building new ships and repairing war damage.

The Americans maintain that in 1940, despite quite a lot of preparation, they were not yet ready to fight a war. The actual cause of the initiative of Congress in this direction was supposedly the military collapse of their ally, France. This expressed itself in feverish activity to supply both warships and merchant vessels by co-ordinating and extending shipbuilding and repair-yard capacity. The result was submarine building on so many fronts that it is almost impossible to reconstruct it in any orderly sequence. This explains the irregular allocation of pennant numbers at the three main construction centres, which were:

- Electric Boat, Groton, Connecticut
- Portsmouth Navy Yard, New Hampshire
- Mare Island Navy Yard, California.

The first contract was placed with Electric Boat, and involved increasing capacity from four to seven slipways at the North Yard. Four more slipways were laid at the newly established South Yard, and the whole project was ready by mid-1941. The later addition of the 'Victory Yard' brought ten more slipways into use by March 1943. By that time, therefore, Electric Boat could build no less than 21 submarines simultaneously. They were launched stern-first and, as there were relatively few fitting-out berths, were extensively finished on the slipway. Most boats were ten months building and a further three fitting out. At the high point of Electric Boat's activity, it employed 12,500 male and female workers in submarine building. During the War, Electric Boat received orders for 115 submarines, of which 82 were completed. The boat with the shortest building time was *Corvina* (SS-226), which took 317 days from keel-laying to commissioning.

Although Electric Boat had a good reputation for submarine building, it is a fact that permanent improvements were first introduced at the Navy Yards, often at the last minute. This meant that most of the submarines built by Electric Boat went to one of the Navy Yards for completion.

At the beginning of the War Portsmouth Navy Yard had the largest capacity: four slipways in an all-weather building hall, a fifth being added soon afterwards. There was also a building dock, operational from March 1943, in which two boats could be constructed simultaneously. One month later, Drydock No 1 also became available for submarine construction, again two at a time, although at the cost of its former repair capability. In contrast to the methods of the Electric Boat Company, slipway time was kept to a minimum so as to reduce overall building time. This was greatly assisted by the prefabrication of large hull sections before the keel was laid. Worker morale was very high, and teams competed with one another to clear slipways as quickly as possible. Three shifts were worked, often with voluntary overtime and extra-shift working. In this way, at the end of 1942, *Cisco* (SS-290) was launched a remarkable 56 days after her keel was laid. Generally, time from keel-laying to commissioning was between seven and eight months, although *Sea Poacher* (SS-406) was built in a record 173 days at the beginning of 1944. It was through such efforts that the Portsmouth yard completed the first wartime contract so quickly that it was already working on another group of new buildings before other yards had finished their first. This was one reason for the confusion and irritation over the allocation of building numbers to the various yards.

During the War, 108 boats were ordered from the Portsmouth Navy Yard, of which 80 were eventually completed. At its peak, it employed 20,000 people, but not all of these were involved in submarine construction.

Many factors aided the building of submarines at this yard. Unlike private firms, Navy Yards did not have to show a profit. Again, there were good relations with the steelworks, so that building materials were available quickly and in quantity. The management consisted mainly of former submarine officers and builders, so that there was a regular interchange of ideas and experience with serving officers, bringing special requirements into effect as rapidly as possible. It should be noted that while each yard favoured its own engine layout, they all used standard diesels from a single supplier.

The Mare Island Navy Yard, lying deep within San Francisco Bay, was the third yard to build submarines in quantity during the inter-war years. Although it had only four slipways, its building capacity was not significantly extended during the War, but it remained one of the most important yards on the West Coast for the repair of ships of all kinds. Some 3,000 workers were employed building submarines. This yard did not produce its own drawings, but used those prepared by Portsmouth Navy Yard. From the wartime building programme, 24 orders were placed with Mare Island, of which eighteen were delivered.

One interesting development was the establishment of a fourth submarine-building facility in September 1940. This was the small Manitowoc SB Co yard on the Great Lakes. As an offshoot of Electric Boat, it worked to their drawings and used their building technology, at least until it had developed its own methods. The yard lay on a fairly narrow river, which made a conventional slipway impossible. So the slipways (which eventually totalled five) were positioned parallel to the river, and approximately at the same level. As had been done with earlier ships, submarines were launched sideways, meeting their native element for the first time with an enormous splash and sometimes rolling as much as 45 degrees. At its peak, this yard employed 7,000 workers, and delivered 28 boats of 47 originally ordered. Shortest building time was nine-and-a-half months for Lamprey (SS-372).

The route by which completed submarines eventually reached the sea was quite adventurous. They were first tested in fresh water trim to nominal depth in Lake Michigan, including periscope. Then everything above the conning-tower's upper edge was stripped down, and the boat was towed up the Chicago River, over which there were many low bridges. After this journey, the boats were loaded on to pontoons at Lockwood, Illinois, carried over the Illinois Waterway, and then down the Mississippi to New Orleans on the Gulf Coast. Surprisingly, this non-stop journey took not more than five or six days. At a base on the Gulf, the periscope was refitted and tested, and the boat then proceeded under its own power through the Panama Canal to the Pacific. As reported, however, other boats went to Electric Boat for completion and preliminary testing. The enthusiasm which the Manitowoc workforce of the time expended on 'their' submarines was lasting, and manifested itself in the maintenance of Cobia (SS-245) as a floating memorial and museum.

Well before the USA's entry into the War, the US Navy had extensively tested materials and equipment for submarines. Among the most interesting and important were the underwater explosion tests carried out from December 1940 on new and manned submarines, in which depth-charges were set off at fixed distances from the boat. For distances less than 90 metres, the crew was taken off and the boat was anchored at a given depth. It was astonishing how little damage was done by these explosions. Even at a distance of only 30 metres, the pressure hull remained intact, although there was considerable interior damage. The first such guinea-pig was Tambor (SS-198), followed by Trout (SS-202) and Gar (SS-206). A further series of explosion tests which took place in 1944 involved Dragonet (SS-293). These concentrated and controlled experiments could not have been replaced by any amount of war experience. They made crews more confident of their boats, showed how much depth-charging they could stand, and what emergency measures would be needed.

Beginning with Tunny (SS-282), all boats were equipped with two distillation plants capable of supplying 1,800 litres per day for drinking water and battery replenishment. Then, from 1942, the use of new high-tensile steels in the Balao Class allowed operational depth to be increased to 120 metres while retaining the 1.5 safety factor.

The introduction to submarine building of the Cramp shipyard in Philadelphia was not especially successful. Originally intended for building cruisers, it had been out of use from 1926 to 1940, but was revived after Pearl Harbor and given a contract to build twelve submarines. The existing long slipways were used to construct two boats at a time, end to end, with the intention of launching both simultaneously. This idea was hindered by poor management, however, and the first delivery was made two years after keel-laying, and then only after fitting out at Portsmouth Navy Yard. Indeed, the best time ever managed was 644 days! Maximum staff was 3,700, and ten boats were delivered out of 29 ordered. Even these were so late that they hardly took any part in the Pacific war. Three more boats were delivered after the War ended.

During the first few months after Pearl Harbor, American submarine crews amassed a great deal of experience which was soon transformed into practical measures in the boats themselves. There was some controversy over this, because not all of these measures were unmixed blessings, but could be advantageous or otherwise depending on circumstances. For example, it was thought that a useful measure for increasing underwater speed was to reduce weight.

It was much the same with opinions on optimum combat methods based on experience gained against the Japanese. The following is only an excerpt from an extensive list of proposals drawn up in 1942:

- remove 100-kW generator and its auxiliary diesel
- remove bridge steering position
- remove all nickel and chrome plating
- reduce conning tower size
- remove forward engine-room hatch and plate over
- remove deck boat
- remove mine anchor-chain cutter
- remove one of the three auxiliary fuel tanks and piping
- remove propeller guards
- remove periscope cladding
- use sheet metal instead of bronze in torpedo tubes

Removal of bulls-eyes (ports) in the conning tower had already taken place before the War began.

In the pre-War classes, the whole area of the periscope base and the bridge was fully plated, not only to improve underwater speed but also to protect the bridge position in high seas. Under wartime conditions, these measures were found to be impracticable. The relatively large plated surfaces made recognition easy for sharp-eyed Japanese lookouts, so the plating was removed and the cigarette deck behind the bridge given a simple railing in order to reduce the overall silhouette. Battle experience proved the importance of access to deck guns and ammunition lockers, and showed that it was prefer-

able to do without streamlined covers over them, and likewise over electronic arrays and lookout positions. Also, removing the bridge steering position enabled 20mm anti-aircraft guns to be fitted.

Some measures, such as increasing the number of flooding ports, shortened diving time. At the beginning of the War, this was about 50 seconds, but wase later reduced to 35 or even 30 seconds.

For the sake of completeness, it should be mentioned that from the beginning of 1944, the Navy Yard at Boston, Massachusetts, in the building of four Tench-Class boats, played a brief and not very successful role in the wartime programme.

In that programme, a total of 339 boats of the three standard classes, Gato, Balao, Tench, were approved, of which 221 had been delivered by the time the War ended. The building of a further 106 was suspended before keels had been laid. Of the remaining twelve boats:

- three were broken up on the slipway
- four were delivered as hulks and later scrapped
- five were eventually completed to a modified design

Some of the things that did *not* happen after the end of the War are still of interest. In February 1945 clearance was given for the building of eighteen submarines, six of which were to be of the Tench Class. The other twelve were to be to a completely new design, for which two studies had been made. Study A envisaged a larger fleet submarine, 98.5 metres in length, with a displacement of 1,800/2,700 tons and an operating depth greater than 150 metres. It is worth noting that a much greater range (19,000 nautical miles) was required, plus a surface speed of 22.5 knots. In addition to the powerful deck armament which was usual by the end of the War, a complement of eighteen torpedoes was proposed, with six short tubes for launching acoustic homing torpedoes. Study B envisaged an even larger boat, of 102.5 metres, displacing 1,960/2,475 tons. However, in view of the impending end to the War, this programme was never started, and was officially suspended in March 1945.

So this phase of wartime submarine construction by the United States came to an end. The submarine force had undergone continuous expansion, as the following sections show.

Gato Class (SS-212)

The design of the *Gato* Class represented the sum of all the experience and improvements of the past, beginning with *Dolphin* and continuing right through to the *Tambor* Class. It is interesting that the first six *Gato*-Class boats of 1941 were originally seen as a continuation of the *Tambor* Class; their names all began with 'G'. In the context of building allocations, it is clear that although the enormous wartime expansion of the submarine fleet began with those six boats, progress actually started with this class. For that reason, SS-212 as lead boat was the first of the three wartime submarine classes.

From a naval point of view, there was virtually no difference between the *Tambor* and *Gato* Classes, but the hull was slightly longer for technical reasons. There was however an improvement in operational depth. After intensive testing, *Gato* was certificated for a safe working depth of 93 metres (300 feet), with a safety factor of 2, without the need for design modifications. The extra 50 feet of water gave the *Gato*-boats a significant advantage over their predecessors.

The great expansion of the fleet at that time meant that more ships of all types were being built in blocks by different yards (four, in the case of the *Gato* Class!). This in turn means that it is not possible to relate pennant numbers to completion dates. Nor are names any more helpful: the first six boats were given names beginning with 'G', but after that the system was abandoned. Production of the *Gato* boats took place from 1942 to 1944, and the first boat to be delivered was actually *Drum* (SS-228), just a few weeks before the attack on Pearl Harbor.

Some aspects of the *Gato* Class were to be of significance for the succeeding classes:

■ The original deck armament, which consisted mostly of not more than a single gun, was very quickly beefed up by the installation of light AA weapons, with machine-guns, 20mm or 40mm guns mounted on specially built platforms. Shields were not included because of weight.

■ Because of the provision of heavier armament and the addition of radar antennae, as well as for other reasons, the conning towers of most submarines were rebuilt, and usually considerably stripped down, often soon after launching.

■ For these reasons, it is true to say that during the Second World War virtually no two submarines were exactly alike. One of the aims of this book is as far as possible to resolve these differences.

This class felt the full weight of Japanese ASW efforts, nineteen boats being lost, most of them in the Pacific. Many of the surviving vessels of this and the other two classes were recommissioned, sometimes twice, after first being taken out of service. Full information about this can be found in the A Tables.

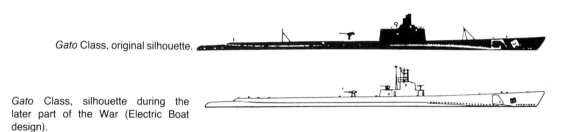

Gato Class, original silhouette.

Gato Class, silhouette during the later part of the War (Electric Boat design).

Gato Class

Pennant numbers	Ships in the class		displacement surfaced	Dimensions m			Output HP	Speed kn	Range Sm/kn	Oil fuel ts	Complement	Original combat systems
SS	planned	completed	submerged	length	beam	draught					Officers/ enlisted	
212 – 284 361 – 364	77	77	2025–2060	95,1	8,3	4,7	5400	20,25	11 000$_{10}$	orig.: 288 in Wartime: 354	6/54 in Wartime: 10/70	orig. 1 - 3in L/50, later various, 6 bow, 4 stern-torpedo tubes 21in (24 Torpedoes, or 2 mines in place of each torpedo up to 40 max)
			2410–2424				2740	8,75	48 Std.$_2$ endurance 75 days			
				Operating depth 93 m								

Powerplant: (a) 4 main and 2 auxiliary diesels operating 2 generators; (b) 4 electric motors driving propeller through reduction gearing.

Towards the end of the War (29 November 1944) the lead boat, *Gato* (SS-212), had a 4in cannon forward of the conning tower, on which was mounted one 40mm and two 20mm anti-aircraft guns. [AB]

Pennant number	Name	FY	Building yard	Keel laid	launched	commissioned / decommissioned	war (and other) loss	reclassified	transferred to	stricken	Remarks
212	*Gato*	41	Electric Boat	5. 10. 40	21. 8. 41	31. 12. 41 / 16. 3. 46				1. 3. 60	1952 / 1. 3. 60 NRT
213	*Greenling*	41	Electric Boat	12. 11. 40	20. 9. 41	21. 1. 42 / 16. 10. 46				1. 3. 60	12. 46 / 1. 3. 60 NRT
214	*Grouper*	41	Electric Boat	28. 12. 40	27. 10. 41	12. 2. 42 / 2. 12. 68		1/51 = SSK-214 6/58 = AGSS-214		2. 12. 68	
215	*Growler*	41	Electric Boat	10. 2. 41	22. 11. 41	20. 3. 42	~ 8. 11. 44				
216	*Grunion*	41	Electric Boat	1. 3. 41	22. 12. 41	11. 4. 42	~ 8. 42				
217	*Guardfish*	41	Electric Boat	1. 4. 41	20. 1. 42	8. 5. 42 / 25. 5. 46				1. 6. 60	18. 6. 48 / 1. 6. 60 NRT
218	*Albacore*	40	Electric Boat	21. 4. 41	17. 2. 42	1. 6. 42	7. 11. 44				
219	*Amberjack*	40	Electric Boat	15. 5. 41	6. 3. 42	19. 6. 42	~ 16. 2. 43				
220	*Barb*	40	Electric Boat	7. 6. 41	2. 4. 42	8. 7. 42 / 12. 2. 47	3. 12. 51 / 5. 2. 54		12/54 Italien		3. 8. 54 / 13. 12. 54 / 1954 GIB
221	*Blackfish*	40	Electric Boat	1. 7. 41	18. 4. 42	22. 7. 42 / 11. 5. 46				1. 9. 58	5. 5. 49 / 19. 5. 54 NRT
222	*Bluefish*	40	Electric Boat	5. 6. 42	21. 2. 43	24. 5. 43 / 12. 2. 47				1. 6. 59	7. 1. 52 / 20. 11. 53
223	*Bonefish*	40	Electric Boat	25. 6. 42	7. 3. 43	31. 5. 43	18. 6. 45				
224	*Cod*	40	Electric Boat	21. 7. 42	21. 3. 43	21. 6. 43 / 22. 6. 46		12/62 = AGSS-224 6/71 = IXSS-224		15. 2. 71	1. 5. 60 / 15. 12. 71 NRT

Pennant number	Name	FY	Building yard	Keel laid	launched	commissioned / decommissioned	war (and other) loss	reclassified	transferred to	stricken	Remarks
225	*Cero*	40	Electric Boat	24. 8. 42	4. 4. 43	4. 7. 43 * / 8. 6. 46	* 4. 2.52 ** 23. 12. 53	12/62 = AGSS-225		30. 6. 67	12. 9. 59 ** / 30. 6. 67 NRT
226	*Corvina*	40	Electric Boat	21. 9. 42	9. 5. 43	6. 8. 43	16. 11. 43				
227	*Darter*	40	Electric Boat	20. 10. 42	6. 6. 43	7. 9. 43	(24. 10. 44)				
228	*Drum*	40	Portsmouth NS	11. 9. 40	12. 5. 41	1. 11. 41 / 16. 2. 46 *		12/62 = AGSS-228		30. 6. 68	18. 3. 47 / 30. 6. 68 NRT
229	*Flying Fish*	40	Portsmouth NS	6. 12. 40	9. 7. 41	10. 12. 41 / 28. 5. 54		11/50 = AGSS-229		1. 8. 58	
230	*Finback*	40	Portsmouth NS	5. 2. 41	25. 8. 41	31. 1. 42 / 21. 4. 50				1. 9. 58	
231	*Haddock*	40	Portsmouth NS	31. 3. 41	20. 10. 41	14. 3. 42 / 12. 2. 47 *	* erneuert 8. 48 ** 5. 52 NRT			1. 6. 60	6. 56 ** / 1960 NRT
232	*Halibut*	40	Portsmouth NS	16. 5. 41	3. 12. 41	10. 4. 42 / 18. 7. 45				8. 5. 46	
233	*Herring*	40	Portsmouth NS	14. 7. 41	15. 1. 42	4. 5. 42	1. 6. 44				
234	*Kingfish*	40	Portsmouth NS	29. 8. 41	2. 3. 42	20. 5. 42 / 9. 3. 46 *				1. 3. 60	6. 10. 47 / 1. 3. 60 NRT
235	*Shad*	40	Portsmouth NS	24. 10. 41	15. 4. 42	12. 6. 42 / 1947 *				1. 4. 60	10. 47 / 1. 4. 60 NRT
236	*Silversides*	40	Mare Island NS	4. 11. 40	26. 8. 41	15. 12. 41 / 17. 4. 46 *		12/62 = AGSS-236		30. 6. 69	15. 10. 47 / 30. 6. 69 NRT
237	*Trigger*	40	Mare Island NS	1. 2. 41	22. 10. 41	30. 1. 42	~ 28. 3. 45				
238	*Wahoo*	40	Mare Island NS	28. 6. 41	14. 2. 42	15. 5. 42	11. 10. 43				

Pennant number	Name	FY	Building yard	Keel laid	launched	commissioned / decommissioned	war (and other) loss	reclassified	transferred to	stricken	Remarks
239	*Whale*	40	Mare Island NS	28. 6. 41	14. 3. 42	1. 6. 42 / 1. 6. 46				1. 3. 60	22. 1. 57 / 1960 NRT
240	*Angler*	40	Electric Boat	9. 11. 42	4. 7. 43	1. 10. 43 / 2. 2. 47	2. 4. 51 / 10. 11. 52	2/53 = SSK-240 8/59 = SS-240 7/63 = AGSS-240 6/71 = IXSS-240		15. 12. 71	10. 9. 53 / 15. 12. 71 from 1968 NRT
241	*Bashaw*	40	Electric Boat	4. 12. 42	25. 7. 43	25. 10. 43 / 20. 6. 49	3. 4. 51 / 10. 5. 52	2/53 = SSK-241 8/59 = SS-241 9/62 = AGSS-241		13. 9. 69	28. 3. 53 / 13. 9. 69
242	*Bluegill*	40	Electric Boat	7. 12. 42	8. 8. 43	11. 11. 43 / 1. 3. 46	3. 5. 51 / 7. 7. 52	2/53 = SSK-242 8/59 = SS-242 4/66 = AGSS-242		28. 6. 69	2. 5. 53 / 28. 6. 69
243	*Bream*	40	Electric Boat	5. 2. 43	17. 10. 43	24. 1. 44 / 31. 1. 46	5. 6. 51 / 10. 9. 52	2/53 = SSK-243 8/59 = SS-243 4/65 = AGSS-243		28. 6. 69	20. 6. 53 / 28. 6. 69
244	*Cavalla*	40	Electric Boat	4. 3. 43	14. 11. 43	29. 2. 44 / 16. 3. 46	10. 4. 51 / 3. 9. 52	2/53 = SSK-244 8/59 = SS-244 7/63 = AGSS-244		30. 12. 69	15. 7. 53 / 30. 12. 69 from 1968 NRT
245	*Cobia*	40	Electric Boat	17. 3. 43	28. 11. 43	29. 3. 44 / 22. 5. 46	6. 7. 51 / 19. 3. 54	12/62 = AGSS-245		1. 7. 70	12. 9. 59 / 1. 7. 70 from 1953 NRT

Pennant number	Name	FY	Building yard	Keel laid	launched	commissioned / decommissioned	war (and other) loss	reclassified	transferred to	stricken	Remarks
246	*Croaker*	40	Electric Boat	1. 4. 43	19. 12. 43	21. 4. 44 * / 15. 6. 46	7. 5. 51 ** / 18. 3. 53	4/53 = SSK-246 8/59 = SS-246 5/67 = AGSS-246 6/71 = IXSS-244		20. 12. 71	11. 12. 53 ** 20. 12. 71 from 1968 NRT
247	*Dace*	40	Electric Boat	22. 7. 42	25. 4. 43	23. 7. 43 * / 12. 2. 47	8. 8. 51 ** / 15. 1. 54		1/55 Italy	15. 10. 72	20. 10. 54 ** 31. 1. 55 1955 GIB
248	*Dorado*	40	Electric Boat	27. 8. 42	23. 5. 43	28. 8. 43	12. 10. 43				
249	*Flasher*	40	Electric Boat	30. 9. 42	20. 6. 43	25. 9. 43 / 16. 3. 46				1. 6. 59	
250	*Flier*	40	Electric Boat	30. 10. 42	11. 7. 43	18. 10. 43	13. 8. 44				
251	*Flounder*	40	Electric Boat	5. 12. 42	22. 8. 43	29. 11. 43 / 12. 2. 47				1. 6. 59	
252	*Gabilan*	40	Electric Boat	5. 1. 43	19. 9. 43	28. 12. 43 / 23. 2. 46				1. 6. 59	
253	*Gunnel*	40	Electric Boat	21. 7. 41	17. 5. 42	20. 8. 42 / 18. 5. 46				1. 9. 58	
254	*Gurnard*	40	Electric Boat	2. 9. 41	1. 6. 42	18. 9. 42 * / 27. 11. 45				1. 5. 61	4. 49 * 6. 60 NRT
255	*Haddo*	40	Electric Boat	1. 10. 41	21. 6. 42	9. 10. 42 / 16. 2. 46				1. 8. 58	
256	*Hake*	40	Electric Boat	1. 11. 41	17. 7. 42	30. 10. 42 / 13. 7. 46 *		12/62 = AGSS-256		19. 4. 68	15. 10. 56 * 19. 4. 68 NRT
257	*Harder*	40	Electric Boat	1. 12. 41	19. 8. 42	2. 12. 42	24. 8. 44				
258	*Hoe*	40	Electric Boat	2. 1. 42	17. 9. 42	16. 12. 42 * / 7. 8. 46				1. 5. 60	9. 56 * 15. 4. 60 NRT
259	*Jack*	40	Electric Boat	2. 2. 42	16. 10. 42	6. 1. 43 * / 8. 6. 46			4/58 Greece	1. 9. 67	20. 12. 57 * 21. 4. 58 1958 FL Sn

Pennant number	Name	FY	Building yard	Keel laid	launched	commissioned / decommissioned	war (and other) loss	reclassified	transferred to	stricken	Remarks
260	Lapon	40	Electric Boat	21. 2. 42	27. 10. 42	23. 1. 43 / 25. 7. 46			8/57 Greece	31. 12. 75	13. 4. 57 / 10. 8. 57 1957 FL Sn
261	Mingo	40	Electric Boat	21. 3. 42	30. 11. 42	12. 2. 43 / 1. 47			8/55 Japan	20. 2. 71	20. 5. 55 / 15. 8. 55•
262	Muskallunge	40	Electric Boat	7. 4. 42	13. 12. 42	15. 3. 43 / 29. 1. 47			1/57 Brazil	1. 12. 67	31. 8. 56 / 18. 1. 57
263	Paddle	40	Electric Boat	1. 5. 42	30. 12. 42	29. 3. 43 / 1. 2. 46			1/57 Brazil	30. 6. 68	31. 8. 56 / 18. 1. 57
264	Pargo	40	Electric Boat	21. 5. 42	24. 1. 43	26. 4. 43 / 12. 6. 46				1. 12. 60	12. 6. 46 / 1. 12. 60 NRT
265	Peto	40	Manitowoc	18. 6. 41	30. 4. 42	21. 11. 42 / 25. 12. 42	1. 43 / 25. 6. 46			1. 8. 60	11. 56 / 1. 8. 60 NRT
266	Pogy	40	Manitowoc	15. 9. 41	23. 6. 42	10. 1. 43 / 1. 2. 43				1. 9. 58	12. 2. 43 / 20. 7. 46
267	Pompon	40	Manitowoc	26. 11. 41	15. 8. 42	17. 3. 43 / 11. 5. 46		12/51 = SSR-267		1. 4. 60	15. 6. 53 / 1. 4. 60
268	Puffer	40	Manitowoc	16. 2. 42	22. 11. 42	27. 4. 43 / 28. 6. 46				1. 7. 60	1946 / 10. 6. 60 NRT
269	Rasher	40	Manitowoc	4. 5. 42	20. 12. 42	8. 6. 43 / 22. 6. 46	14. 12. 51 / 28. 5. 52	12/51 = SSR-269 7/60 = AGSS-269 6/71 = IXSS-269		20. 12. 71	22. 7. 53 / 20. 12. 71 from 1967 NRT
270	Raton	40	Manitowoc	29. 5. 42	24. 1. 43	13. 7. 43 / 3. 50		7/52 = SSR-270 7/60 = AGSS-270		28. 6. 69	21. 9. 53 / 28. 6. 69
271	Ray	40	Manitowoc	20. 7. 42	28. 2. 43	27. 7. 43 / 12. 2. 47	9. 1. 53 / 15. 5. 67	1/51 = SSR-271		1. 7. 70	30. 6. 67 / 1. 7. 70
272	Redfin	40	Manitowoc	3. 9. 42	4. 4. 43	31. 8. 43 / 1. 11. 46	9. 1. 53 / 15. 5. 67	1/51 = SSR-272 8/59 = SS-272 6/63 = AGSS-272		1. 7. 70	30. 6. 67 / 1. 7. 70 NRT

Pennant number	Name	FY	Building yard	Keel laid	launched	commissioned / decommissioned	war (and other) loss	reclassified	transferred to	stricken	Remarks
273	Robalo	40	Manitowoc	24. 10. 42	9. 5. 43	28. 9. 43	26. 7. 42				
274	Rock	40	Manitowoc	23. 12. 42	20. 6. 43	26. 10. 43 / 1. 5. 46		7/52 = SSR-274 12/59 = AGSS-274		13. 9. 69	12. 10. 53 13. 9. 69
275	Runner	40	Portsmouth NS	8. 12. 41	30. 5. 42	30. 7. 42	~ 6. 43				
276	Sawfish	40	Portsmouth NS	20. 1. 42	23. 6. 42	26. 8. 42 / 20. 6. 46				1. 4. 60	15. 5. 47 1. 4. 60 NRT
277	Scamp	40	Portsmouth NS	6. 3. 42	20. 7. 42	18. 9. 42	~ 16. 11. 44				
278	Scorpion	40	Portsmouth NS	20. 3. 42	20. 7. 42	1. 10. 42	~ 1. 44				
279	Snook	40	Portsmouth NS	17. 4. 42	15. 8. 42	24. 10. 42	~ 8. 4. 45				
280	Steelhead	40	Portsmouth NS	1. 6. 42	11. 9. 42	7. 12. 42 / 29. 6. 46				1. 4. 60	12. 11. 47 1. 4. 60 NRT
281	Sunfish	40	Mare Island NS	25. 9. 41	2. 5. 42	15. 7. 42 / 26. 12. 45				1. 5. 60	4. 49 1. 5. 60 NRT
282	Tunny	40	Mare Island NS	10. 11. 41	30. 6. 42	1. 9. 42 / 12. 2. 46	25. 2. 52 / 30. 4. 52	7/52 = SSG-282 5/65 = SS-282 10/66 = APSS-282 1/69 = LPSS-282		30. 6. 69	6. 3. 53 28. 6. 69
283	Tinosa	40	Mare Island NS	21. 2. 42	7. 10. 42	15. 1. 43 / 23. 6. 49				1. 9. 58	4. 1. 52 2. 12. 53
284	Tullibee	40	Mare Island NS	1. 4. 42	11. 11. 42	15. 2. 43	26. 3. 44				
361	Golet	42	Manitowoc	27. 1. 43	1. 8. 43	30. 11. 43	14. 6. 44				

Pennant number	Name	FY	Building yard	Keel laid	launched	commissioned / decommissioned	war (and other) loss	reclassified	transferred to	stricken	Remarks
362	*Guavina*	42	Manitowoc	3. 3. 43	29. 8. 43	23. 12. 43 *—* 1946	1. 2. 50 *—** 27. 3. 59	8/48 = SSO-362 12/51 = AGSS-362 6/57 = AOSS-362		30. 6. 67	**2. 60 30. 6. 67 NRT
363	*Guitarro*	42	Manitowoc	7. 4. 43	26. 9. 43	26. 1. 44 *—** 6. 12. 45	6. 2. 52 *—** 22. 9. 53		8/54 Turkey	1. 1. 72	15. 5. 54 **— 7. 8. 54 1954 FL Sn
364	*Hammer-head*	42	Manitowoc	5. 5. 43	24. 10. 43	1. 3. 44 *—* 9. 2. 46	6. 2. 52 *—** 21. 8. 53		10/54 Turkey	1. 1. 72	16. 7. 54 **— 23. 10. 54 1954 Fl Sn

During the first post-War years there was considerable variation in type and location of pennant numbers. Here, we see *Gato*, five months before decommissioning, with her number painted, unusually, in black. The heavy armament includes a 5in deck gun aft of the conning tower, plus two 40mm and one 20mm AA guns. [LvG]

Greenling (SS-213), seen here with her original conning tower and 3in armament. [USN]

This photograph of *Grouper* (SS-214), taken on 17 July 1945, shows a good example of Measure 32/3SS-B camouflage. The radar antennae are SJ-1 and SV types. [USN]

Guardfish (SS-217), 15 April 1942, a few weeks before commissioning, near the Electric Boat shipyard. Note the absence of deck armament. [USN]

Undated photograph of *Barb* (SS-220). [USN] ▼

Shortly before the end of the War, a photo-record was prepared at the Mare Island Navy Yard, from which these four photographs (see also the three on the next page) come. The boat shown is *Cero* (SS-225), with Measure 32 camouflage. By this time (13 February 1945), submarines had normally dispensed with propeller guards. [USN]

A post-War photograph of *Finback* (SS-230), no longer fitted with 20mm Oerlikon. However, she still has the foredeck-mounted JP hydrophone, which had to be rotated by hand from inside the boat. [AB]

Halibut (SS-232) on 20 May 1942, a month after commissioning. Original silhouette with the 3in deck gun aft of the conning tower. [USN]

Kingfish (SS-234), seen here off Mare Island on 5 June 1943, with 4in gun forward of the stripped-down conning tower. [USN]

Shad (SS-235), 2 March 1944. [USN] ▶

Silversides (SS-236) in August 1944, with 4in and 40mm AA guns. [USN]

Whale (SS-239), 21 April 1945; a rare example of the 20mm AA gun being mounted forward of the conning tower. [USN]
▶

83

In her second incarnation *Silversides* (SS-236) remained active from October 1947 to 1969, being reclassified AGSS in 1962. This photograph was taken in about 1960, and shows the sizeable extension for various equipment mounted on the conning tower. AA weapons have been banished from the cigarette deck, but the evidence of wartime experience against the Japanese can be seen in the tally painted on the side of the conning tower. Note the radar antennae: there is a barely visible SD antenna (far right, on the forward mast), and a more modern SJ antenna. [AB]

Whale (S-239), 21 April 1945, exercising the 12.7cm L/25 deck gun. [AB]

Cavalla (SS-244), *circa* 1946. [AB]

Cobia (AGSS-245) in 1965, seen here in her final role as a training hulk with the Naval Reserve Force. Her appearance is more or less typical of all such immobilized vessels. [E. Schmidt]

Post-War photograph of *Dace* (SS-247). [AB]

Gurnard (SS-254). [AB]

A good idea of the usual underwater hull form of these boats can be obtained from this launch photograph of *Cobia* (SS-245) at Electric Boat on 28 November 1943. [USN]

This photograph of *Jack* (SS-259) on 17 December 1943 shows details of the conning tower. Circles indicate modifications made while she was still in the yard. On the left mast the SD radar antenna can just be seen, in front of the later SJ antenna. Both periscopes are in the up position. [USN] ▼

Mingo (SS-261), one month before being transferred to Japan in 1955, still wearing her wartime camouflage, but with only the 5in L/25 gun as armament. An SS radar can be seen on the main mast. [USN]

Paddle (SS-263), with the early SJ radar antenna,13 February 1944. [AB]

◄

Submarines built at the Manitowoc yard held their 'sea trials' in the Great Lakes. Here we see Pompon (SS-267) on trials in Lake Michigan, April 1943. [USN]

The Manitowoc yard in Wisconsin launched its boats sideways, as with Peto (SS-265), seen here on 30 April 1942 with original conning tower. [USN]

Side elevation of *Rasher* (SS-269), soon after delivery, with 3in gun on high mounting, plus two 20mm AA guns. [USN]

▲
Another Lake Michigan shot, August 1943: *Ray* (SS-271), with 4in gun. [USN]

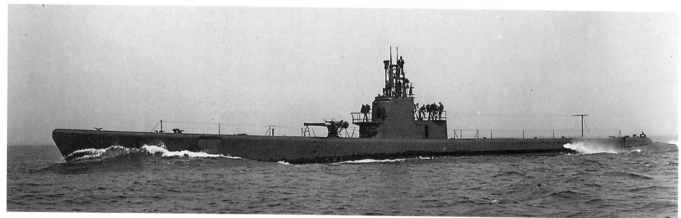

Rock (SS-274), with 4in deck gun. [AB]

Tunny (SS-282). [AB]

Navy identification photograph of *Tinosa* (SS-283), 5 March 1943, with 4in deck gun and two 20mm AA guns with shield. [USN]

Ten years later: *Tinosa*, 15 January 1953, still has her 5in gun, now aft of the conning tower, plus two 40mm AA guns. In the background is the destroyer escort *Currier* (DE-700). [AB]

Side launch of *Hammerhead* (SS-364) at Manitowoc, 24 October 1943. During the War *Gato* Class boats were built with stripped-down conning tower and two cigarette decks. [USN]

Balao Class (SS-285)

There was only one significant difference between the *Gato* and *Balao* Classes, but it was unique, as well as being one of the best-kept secrets of the submarine war. Through the use of high-tensile steels, operational depth was increased to 122 metres, which greatly improved fighting capabilitiy. Other small differences that were introduced had already been tried to some extent in *Gato*-Class boats.

Total delivery of this class was 120; many more being suspended or cancelled. Most came into service between 1943 and 1945, and the fact that only nine were lost is usually attributed to their relatively late entry into the War.

After the War many of the *Balao* boats were rebuilt in the course of the various modernization programmes described in following sections.

Balao Class

Pennant numbers SS	Ships in the class		displacement surfaced submerged	Dimensions m			Output HP	Speed kn	Range Sm/kn	Oil fuel ts	Complement Officers/ enlisted	Original combat systems
	planned	completed		length	beam	draught						
285 – 352 365 – 378 381 – 416 425 – 426 suspended u.a.m.: 353 – 360 379 – 380 427 – 428 429 – 434	138	120	2010–2075 2415	95,1 Operating depth 122 m	8,3	4,7	5400 2740	20,25 8,75	$11\,000_{10}$ 48 Std.$_2$ endurance 75 days	439	10/70	1 - 4in L/50 or 1 - 5in L/25 6 bow, 4 stern torpedo tubes 21in (24 Torpedoes, or 2 mines in place of 1 torpedo up to 40 max)

Powerplant: (a) 4 main and 1 auxiliary diesel operating 2 generators; (b) 4 electric motors driving propeller through reduction gearing (in some boats, 2 electric motors driving propeller direct).

Balao Class, original appearance.

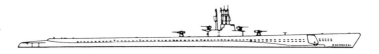

Balao Class, appearance during later part of War.

Balao as AGSS-285, without guns and painted black. An SS-2 radar antenna can be seen on the conning tower which bears the squadron insignia above the pennant number. Photograph taken off Key West, Florida, on 7 March 1961. [USN]

Pennant number	Name	FY	Building yard	Keel laid	launched	commissioned / decommissioned	war (and other) loss	reclassified	transferred to	stricken	Remarks
285	*Balao*	41	Portsmouth NS	26. 6. 42	27. 10. 42	4. 2. 43 * / 20. 8. 46		4/60 = AGSS-285			4. 3. 52 / 11. 7. 63
286	*Billfish*	41	Portsmouth NS	23. 7. 42	12. 11. 42	20. 4. 43 * / 1. 11. 46		12/62 = AGSS-286		1. 4. 68	1. 1. 60 * / 1. 4. 68 NRT
287	*Bowfin*	41	Portsmouth NS	23. 7. 42	7. 12. 42	1. 5. 43 * / 12. 2. 47	27. 7.51 ** / 22. 4. 54			1. 12. 71	10. 6. 60 ** / 1. 12. 71 NRT
288	*Cabrilla*	41	Portsmouth NS	18. 8. 42	24. 12. 42	24. 5. 43 * / 7. 8. 46		12/62 = AGSS-288		30. 6. 68	5. 60 * / 30. 6. 68 NRT
289	*Capelin*	41	Portsmouth NS	14. 9. 42	20. 1. 43	4. 6. 43	~ 12. 43				
290	*Cisco*	41	Portsmouth NS	29. 10. 42	24. 12. 42	10. 5. 43	28. 9. 43				
291	*Crevalle*	41	Portsmouth NS	14. 11. 42	22. 2. 43	24. 6. 43 * / 20. 7. 46	6. 9.51 ** / 19. 8.55	4/60 = AGSS-291	11. 4. 57 ** / 9. 3. 62 ***	15. 4. 68	1962 / 1968 NRT
292	*Devilfish*	41	Cramp	31. 3. 42	30. 5. 43	1. 9. 44 / 30. 9. 46		12/62 = AGSS-292		1. 3. 67	
293	*Dragonet*	41	Cramp	28. 4. 42	18. 4. 43	6. 3. 44 / 16. 4. 46				1. 6. 61	
294	*Escolar*	41	Cramp	10. 6. 42	18. 4. 43	2. 6. 44	~ 10. 44				
295	*Hackleback*	41	Cramp	15. 8. 42	30. 5. 43	7. 11. 44 / 20. 3. 46		12/62 = AGSS-295		·1. 3. 67	
296	*Lancetfish*	41	Cramp	30. 9. 42	15. 8. 43	12. 2. 45 / 24. 3. 45				9. 6. 58	
297	*Ling*	41	Cramp	2. 11. 42	15. 8. 43	8. 6. 45 * / 26. 10. 46		12/62 = AGSS-297 / 6/71 = IXSS-297		1. 12. 71	3. 60 * / 1. 12. 71

Pennant number	Name	FY	Building yard	Keel laid	launched	commissioned / decommissioned	war (and other) loss	reclassified	transferred to	stricken	Remarks
298	Lionfish	41	Cramp	15. 12. 42	7. 11. 43	1. 11. 44 * / 16. 1. 46	31. 1. 51 ** / 15. 12. 53	12/62 = AGSS-298 6/71 = IXSS-298		20. 12. 71	1. 3. 60 ** 20. 12. 71
299	Manta	41	Cramp	15. 1. 43	7. 11. 43	18. 12. 44 * / 10. 1. 46	2. 8. 49 ** / 6. 12. 55	8/49 = AGSS-299		30. 6. 67	4. 60 ** 30. 6. 67 NRT
300	Moray	41	Cramp	21. 4. 43	14. 5. 44	26. 1. 45 / 12. 4. 46		12/62 = AGSS-300		1. 4. 67	
301	Roncador	41	Cramp	21. 4. 43	14. 5. 44	27. 3. 45 * / 1. 6. 46		12/62 = AGSS-301 6/71 = IXSS-301		1. 12. 71	2. 60 * 1. 12. 71 NRT
302	Sabalo	41	Cramp	5. 6. 43	4. 6. 44	19. 6. 45 * / 7. 8. 46				1. 7. 71	6. 51 * 1. 7. 71 1952 Fl Sn
303	Sablefish	41	Cramp	5. 6. 43	4. 6. 44	18. 12. 45 / 1. 11. 69		6/69 = AGSS-303		1. 11. 69	1951 Fl Sn
304	Seahorse	41	Mare Island NS	1. 7. 42	9. 1. 43	31. 3. 43 / 2. 3. 46		12/62 = AGSS-304		1. 3. 67	
305	Skate	41	Mare Island NS	1. 8. 42	4. 3. 43	15. 4. 43 / 11. 12. 46	(5. 10. 48) Bikini			21. 10. 48	
306	Tang	41	Mare Island NS	15. 1. 43	17. 8. 43	15. 10. 43	24. 10. 44				
307	Tilefish	41	Mare Island NS	10. 3. 43	25. 10. 43	15. 12. 43 * / 12. 10. 59			5/60 Venezuela	1. 12. 60	30. 1. 60 * 4. 5. 60 1960 Fl Sn
308	Apogon (ex-Abadejo)	42	Electric Boat	9. 12. 42	10. 3. 43	16. 7. 43 / 29. 9. 43	(25. 7. 46) Bikini			25. 2. 47	
309	Aspro (ex-Acedia)	42	Electric Boat	27. 12. 42	7. 4. 43	31. 7. 43 * / 10. 1. 46		7/60 = AGSS-309		1. 9. 62	23. 9. 51 * 7. 9. 62
310	Batfish (ex-Acoupa)	42	Electric Boat	27. 12. 42	5. 5. 43	21. 8. 43 * / 6. 4. 46		12/62 = AGSS-310		1. 11. 69	7. 3. 52 * 1. 11. 69 1960 NRT

Pennant number	Name	FY	Building yard	Keel laid	launched	commissioned / decommissioned	war (and other) loss	reclassified	transferred to	stricken	Remarks
311	*Archerfish*	42	Electric Boat	22. 1. 43	28. 5. 43	4. 9. 43 / 12. 6. 46	7. 3. 52 / 21. 10. 55	2/60 = AGSS-311		1. 5. 68	1. 8. 57 / 1. 5. 68
312	*Burrfish* (ex-Arnillo)	42	Electric Boat	24. 2. 43	18. 6. 43	13. 9. 43 / 10. 10. 46	2. 11. 48 / 17. 12. 56	2/49 = SSR-312 1/61 = SS-312	5/61 Canada	31. 7. 69	17. 1. 61 / 11. 5. 61
313	*Perch*	42	Electric Boat	5. 1. 43	12. 9. 43	7. 1. 44 / 1. 47	20. 5. 48 / 31. 3. 60	1/48 = SSP-313 1/50 = ASSP-313 10/56 = APSS-313 1/69 = LPSS-313 6/71 = IXSS-313	11. 11. 61 / 27. 5. 67	1. 12. 71	30. 6. 67 / 1. 12. 71 NRT
314	*Shark*	42	Electric Boat	28. 1. 43	17. 10. 43	14. 2. 44	24. 10. 44				
315	*Sealion*	42	Electric Boat	25. 2. 43	31. 10. 43	8. 3. 44 / 16. 2. 46	2. 11. 48 / 30. 6. 60	4/48 = SSP-315 1/50 = ASSP-315 10/56 = APSS-315 1/69 = LPSS-315	30. 6. 60 / 28. 8. 61 NRT	15. 3. 77	20. 10. 61 / 20. 2. 70
316	*Barbel*	42	Electric Boat	11. 3. 43	14. 11. 43	3. 4. 44	4. 2. 45				
317	*Barbero*	42	Electric Boat	25. 3. 43	12. 12. 43	29. 4. 44 / 30. 6. 50		4/48 = SSA-317 1/50 = ASSA-317 10/55 = SSG-317		1. 7. 64	28. 10. 55 / 30. 6. 64
318	*Baya*	42	Electric Boat	8. 4. 43	2. 1. 44	20. 5. 44 / 14. 5. 46		8/49 = AGSS-318		30. 10. 72	10. 2. 48 / 30. 10. 72
319	*Becuna*	42	Electric Boat	29. 4. 43	30. 1. 44	27. 5. 44 / 7. 11. 69		10/69 = AGSS-319 6/71 = SS-319		15. 8. 73	1951 G IA

Pennant number	Name	FY	Building yard	Keel laid	launched	commissioned / decommissioned	war (and other) loss	reclassified	transferred to	Stricken	Remarks
320	*Bergall*	42	Electric Boat	13. 5. 43	16. 2. 44	12. 6. 44 / 18. 10. 58			10/58 Turkey	1. 2. 73	1952 FL Sn
321	*Besugo*	42	Electric Boat	27. 5. 43	27. 2. 44	19. 6. 44 / 21. 3. 58		12/62 = AGSS-321	3/66 Italy	15. 11. 75	1966 / 31. 3. 66 / 1966 FL Sn
322	*Blackfin*	42	Electric Boat	10. 6. 43	12. 3. 44	4. 7. 44 / 19. 11. 48				15. 9. 72	15. 5. 51 / 15. 9. 72 / 1951 G IA
323	*Caiman* (ex-Blan-quillo)	42	Electric Boat	24. 6. 43	30. 3. 44	17. 7. 44 / 30. 6. 72			6/72 Turkey	30. 6. 72	1951 G IA
324	*Blenny*	42	Electric Boat	8. 7. 43	9. 4. 44	27. 7. 44 / 7. 11. 69		10/69 = AGSS-324 6/71 = SS-324		15. 8. 73	1951 G IA 1988 again NISMF, Norfolk, Va.
325	*Blower*	42	Electric Boat	15. 7. 43	23. 4. 44	10. 8. 44 / 16. 11. 50			11/50 Turkey	20. 12. 50	1950 FL Sn
326	*Blueback*	42	Electric Boat	29. 7. 43	7. 5. 44	28. 8. 44 / 23. 5. 48			5/48 Turkey	23. 5. 48	1953 FL Sn
327	*Boarfish*	42	Electric Boat	12. 8. 43	21. 5. 44	23. 9. 44 / 23. 5. 48			5/48 Turkey	23. 5. 48	1953 FL Sn
328	*Charr* (ex-Bo-caccio)	42	Electric Boat	26. 8. 43	28. 5. 44	23. 9. 44 / 28. 6. 69		7/66 = AGSS-328 6/71 = IXSS-328		20. 12. 71	28. 6. 69 / 20. 12. 71 NRT / 1951 FL Sn
329	*Chub* (ex-Bonachi)	42	Electric Boat	16. 9. 43	18. 6. 44	21. 10. 44 / 23. 5. 48			5/48 Turkey	23. 5. 48	1953 FL Sn
330	*Brill*	42	Electric Boat	23. 9. 43	25. 6. 44	26. 10. 44 / 23. 5. 48			5/48 Turkey	23. 5. 48	1953 FL Sn
331	*Bugara*	42	Electric Boat	21. 10. 43	2. 7. 44	15. 11. 44 / 1. 10. 70		6/69 = AGSS-331 10/69 = SS-331		1. 10. 70	1951 FL Sn
332	*Bullhead*	42	Electric Boat	21. 10. 43	16. 7. 44	4. 12. 44	~ 6. 8. 45				
333	*Bumper*	42	Electric Boat	4. 11. 43	6. 8. 44	9. 12. 44 / 16. 11. 50			11/50 Turkey	20. 12. 50	1950 FL Sn

Pennant number	Name	FY	Building yard	Keel laid	launched	commissioned / decommissioned	war (and other) loss	reclassified	transferred to	stricken	Remarks
334	*Cabezon*	42	Electric Boat	18. 11. 43	27. 8. 44	30. 12. 44 24. 10. 53		12/62 = AGSS-334		15. 5. 70	4. 60 15. 5. 70 NRT
335	*Dentuda* (ex-Capidoli)	42	Electric Boat	18. 11. 43	10. 9. 44	30. 12. 44 11. 12. 46		12/62 = AGSS-335		30. 6. 67	11. 12. 46 30. 6. 67 NRT
336	*Capitaine*	42	Electric Boat	2. 12. 43	1. 10. 44	26. 1. 45 10. 2. 50		7/60 = AGSS-336	3/66 Italy	5. 12. 77	23. 2. 57 4. 3. 66 1966 FL Sn
337	*Carbonero*	42	Electric Boat	16. 12. 43	15. 10. 44	7. 2. 45 1. 12. 70		6/69 = AGSS-337 10/69 = SS-337		1. 12. 70	guided missile launcher fitted 1949
338	*Carp*	42	Electric Boat	23. 12. 43	12. 11. 44	28. 2. 45 18. 3. 68		5/68 = AGSS-338 6/71 = IXSS-338		20. 12. 71	18. 3. 68 20. 12. 71 NRT 1952 FL Sn
339	*Catfish*	42	Electric Boat	6. 1. 44	19. 11. 44	19. 3. 45 1. 7. 71			7/71 Argentina	1. 7. 71	1949 G II
340	*Entemedor* (ex-Chickwick)	42	Electric Boat	3. 2. 44	17. 12. 44	6. 4. 45 10. 12. 48			7/72 Turkey	1. 8. 73	24. 10. 50 31. 7. 72 1952 G IIA
341	*Chivo*	42	Electric Boat	21. 2. 44	14. 1. 45	28. 4. 45 1. 7. 71			7/71 Argentina	1. 7. 71	1951 G IA
342	*Chopper*	42	Electric Boat	2. 3. 44	4. 2. 45	25. 5. 45 27. 8. 69		9/69 = AGSS-342 6/71 = IXSS-342			27. 8. 69 1. 10. 71 NRT 1951 G IA
343	*Clamagore*	42	Electric Boat	16. 3. 44	25. 2. 45	28. 6. 45 12. 6. 75				12. 6. 75	1948 G II 1962 G III
344	*Cobbler*	42	Electric Boat	3. 4. 44	1. 4. 45	8. 8. 45 21. 11. 73			11/73 Turkey	21. 11. 73	1949 G II 1962 G III
345	*Cochino*	42	Electric Boat	13. 4. 44	20. 4. 45	25. 8. 45	(26. 8. 49)				1949 G II
346	*Corporal*	42	Electric Boat	27. 4. 44	10. 6. 45	9. 11. 45 21. 11. 73			11/73 Turkey	21. 11. 73	1948 G II 1962 G III
347	*Cubera*	42	Electric Boat	11. 5. 44	17. 6. 45	19. 12. 45 5. 11. 72			1/72 Venezuela	5. 1. 72	1948 G II

Pennant number	Name	FY	Building yard	Keel laid	launched	commissioned / decommissioned	war (and other) loss	reclassified	transferred to	stricken	Remarks
348	*Cusk*	42	Electric Boat	25. 5. 44	28. 7. 45	5. 2. 46 / 24. 9. 69		1/48 = SSG-348 7/54 = SS-348 6/69 = AGSS-348		24. 9. 69	1954 FL Sn
349	*Diodon*	42	Electric Boat	1. 6. 44	10. 9. 45	18. 3. 46 / 15. 1. 71				15. 1. 71	1948 G II
350	*Dogfish*	42	Electric Boat	22. 6. 44	27. 10. 45	29. 4. 46 / 28. 7. 72			7/72 Brazil	28. 7. 72	1948 G II
351	*Greenfish* (ex-Doncella)	42	Electric Boat	29. 6. 44	21. 12. 45	7. 6. 46 / 19. 12. 73			12/73 Brazil	19. 12. 73	1948 G II 1961 G III
352	*Halfbeak* (ex-Dory)	42	Electric Boat	6. 7. 44	19. 2. 46	22. 7. 46 / 1. 7. 71				1. 7. 71	1948 G II
365	*Hardhead*	42	Manitowoc	7. 7. 43	12. 12. 43	18. 4. 44 * / 10. 5. 46	6. 2.52 ** / 22. 5. 52		7/72 Greece	26. 7. 72	24. 3. 53 ** 26. 7. 72 1953 G IIA
366	*Hawkbill*	42	Manitowoc	7. 8. 43	9. 1. 44	17. 5. 44 * / 20. 9. 66			4/53 Netherlands	20. 2. 70	1953 * 21. 4. 53 1953 G IB
367	*Icefish*	42	Manitowoc	4. 9. 43	20. 2. 44	10. 6. 44 * / 21. 6. 46	5. 5.52 ** / 29. 7. 52		2/53 Netherlands	15. 7. 71	10. 12. 52 ** 21. 2. 53 1953 G IB
368	*Jallao*	42	Manitowoc	29. 9. 43	12. 3. 44	8. 7. 44 * / 30. 9. 46			6/74 Spain	26. 7. 74	4. 12. 53 * 26. 6. 74 1954 G IIA
369	*Kete*	42	Manitowoc	25. 10. 43	9. 4. 44	31. 7. 44	~ 20. 3. 45				
370	*Kraken*	42	Manitowoc	13. 12. 43	30. 4. 44	8. 9. 44 * / 4. 5. 46			10/59 Spain	18. 11. 74	1959 * 24. 10. 59 1959 FL Sn
371	*Lagarto*	42	Manitowoc	12. 1. 44	28. 5. 44	14. 10. 44	4. 5. 45				
372	*Lamprey*	42	Manitowoc	22. 2. 44	18. 6. 44	17. 11. 44 * / 3. 6. 46			8/60 Argentina	1. 9. 71	1960 * 21. 8. 60

Pennant number	Name	FY	Building yard	Keel laid	launched	commissioned / decommissioned	war (and other) loss	reclassified	transferred to	stricken	Remarks
373	*Lizardfish*	42	Manitowoc	14. 3. 44	16. 7. 44	30. 12. 44 / 24. 6. 46			1/60 Italy		1959 / 9. 1. 60 / 1959 FL Sn
374	*Loggerhead*	42	Manitowoc	1. 4. 44	13. 8. 44	9. 2. 45 / 1946		12/62 = AGSS-374		30. 6. 67	1. 6. 60 / 30. 6. 67 NRT
375	*Macabi*	42	Manitowoc	1. 5. 44	19. 9. 44	29. 3. 45 / 16. 6. 46			8/60 Argentina	1. 9. 71	6. 5. 60 / 11. 8. 60
376	*Mapiro*	42	Manitowoc	30. 5. 44	9. 11. 44	30. 4. 45 / 16. 3. 46			3/60 Turkey	1. 8. 73	1960 / 18. 3. 60 / 1960 FL Sn
377	*Menhaden*	42	Manitowoc	21. 6. 44	20. 12. 44	22. 6. 45 / 31. 5. 46	7. 8. 51 / 13. 8. 52			15. 8. 73	6. 3. 53 / 13. 8. 71 / 1953 G IIA
378	*Mero*	42	Manitowoc	22. 7. 44	17. 1. 45	17. 8. 45 / 15. 6. 46			4/60 Turkey	1. 8. 73	1960 / 20. 4. 60 / 1960 FL Sn
381	*Sand Lance* (ex-Orca, ex-Ojanco)	42	Portsmouth NS	12. 3. 43	25. 6. 43	9. 10. 43 / 14. 2. 46			9/63 Brazil	1. 9. 72	6. 4. 63 / 7. 9. 63
382	*Picuda* (ex-Obispo)	42	Portsmouth NS	15. 3. 43	12. 7. 43	16. 10. 43 / 25. 9. 46			10/72 Spain	18. 11. 74	19. 6. 53 / 1. 10. 72 / 1953 G IIA
383	*Pampanito*	42	Portsmouth NS	15. 3. 43	12. 7. 43	6. 11. 43 / 15. 12. 45		12/62 = AGSS-383 6/71 = IXSS-383		20. 12. 71	4. 60 / 20. 12. 71 NRT
384	*Parche*	42	Portsmouth NS	9. 4. 43	24. 7. 43	20. 11. 43 / 11. 12. 46		12/62 = AGSS-384		8. 11. 69	10. 2. 48 / 8. 11. 69 NRT
385	*Bang*	42	Portsmouth NS	30. 4. 43	30. 8. 43	4. 12. 43 / 12. 2. 47	1. 2. 51 / 15. 5. 52		10/72 Spain	18. 1. 74	4. 10. 52 / 1. 10. 72 / 1952 G IIA
386	*Pilotfish*	42	Portsmouth NS	15. 5. 43	30. 8. 43	16. 12. 43 / 29. 8. 46	(1946) Bikini			25. 2. 47	

Pennant number	Name	FY	Building yard	Keel laid	launched	commissioned / decommissioned	war (and other) loss	reclassified	transferred to	stricken	Remarks
387	*Pintado*	42	Portsmouth NS	7. 5. 43	15. 9. 43	1. 1. 44 / 6. 3. 46		12/62 = AGSS-387		1. 3. 67	
388	*Pipefish*	42	Portsmouth NS	31. 5. 43	12. 10. 43	22. 1. 44 / 19. 3. 46		12/62 = AGSS-388		1. 3. 67	
389	*Piranha*	42	Portsmouth NS	21. 6. 43	27. 10. 43	5. 2. 44 / 31. 5. 46		12/62 = AGSS-389		1. 3. 67	
390	*Plaice*	42	Portsmouth NS	28. 6. 43	15. 11. 43	12. 2. 44 / 11. 47*			9/63 Brazil	1. 4. 73	18. 5. 63* / 7. 9. 63
391	*Pomphret*	42	Portsmouth NS	14. 7. 43	27. 10. 43	19. 2. 44 / 4. 52*			7/71 Turkey	1. 8. 73	5. 12. 52* / 1. 7. 71 / 1953 G IIA
392	*Sterlet* (ex-Pudiano)	42	Portsmouth NS	14. 7. 43	27. 10. 43	4. 3. 44 / 18. 9. 48*				1. 10. 68	26. 8. 50* / 30. 9. 68 / 1952 FL Sn
393	*Queenfish*	42	Portsmouth NS	27. 7. 43	30. 11. 43	11. 3. 44 / 1. 3. 63		7/60 = AGSS-393		1. 3. 63	
394	*Razorback*	42	Portsmouth NS	9. 9. 43	27. 1. 44	3. 4. 44 / 8. 52*			11/70 Turkey	30. 11. 70	1954* / 30. 11. 70 / 1954 G IIA
395	*Redfish*	42	Portsmouth NS	9. 9. 43	27. 1. 44	12. 4. 44 / 27. 6. 68		7/60 = AGSS-395		30. 6. 68	
396	*Ronquil*	42	Portsmouth NS	9. 9. 43	27. 1. 44	22. 4. 44 / 5. 52*			7/71 Spain	1. 7. 71	16. 1. 53* / 1. 7. 71 / 1953 G IIA
397	*Scabbard-fish*	42	Portsmouth NS	27. 9. 43	27. 1. 44	29. 4. 44 / 5. 1. 48*			2/65 Greece	31. 1. 76	24. 10. 64* / 26. 2. 65 / 1965 FL Sn
398	*Segundo*	42	Portsmouth NS	14. 10. 43	5. 2. 44	9. 5. 44 / 1. 8. 70				8. 8. 70	1951 FL Sn
399	*Sea Cat*	42	Portsmouth NS	30. 10. 43	21. 2. 44	16. 5. 44 / 2. 12. 68		9/49 = AGSS-399 12/51 = SS-399 6/68 = AGSS-399		2. 12. 68	1952 FL Sn

Pennant number	Name	FY	Building yard	Keel laid	launched	commissioned decommissioned	war (and other) loss	reclassified	transferred to	stricken	Remarks
400	Sea Devil	42	Portsmouth NS	18. 11. 43	28. 2. 44	24. 5. 44 * 9. 9. 48	3. 3. 51 * 19. 2. 54 **	7/60 = AGSS-400		1. 4. 64	17. 8. 57 ** 17. 2. 64
401	Sea Dog	42	Portsmouth NS	1. 11. 43	28. 3. 44	3. 6. 44 * 27. 6. 56		12/62 = AGSS-401		2. 12. 68	2. 60 * 2. 12. 68 NRT
402	Sea Fox	42	Portsmouth NS	2. 11. 43	28. 3. 44	13. 6. 44 * 15. 10. 52			12/70 Turkey	14. 12. 70	5. 6. 53 * 14. 12. 70 1953 G IIA
403	Atule	42	Portsmouth NS	2. 12. 43	6. 3. 44	21. 6. 44 * 8. 9. 47		10/69 = AGSS-403 6/71 = SS-403	7/74 Peru	15. 8. 73	8. 3. 51 * 1951 G IA
404	Spikefish (ex-Shiner)	42	Portsmouth NS	29. 1. 44	26. 4. 44	30. 6. 44 2. 4. 63		7/62 = AGSS-404		1. 5. 63	
405	Sea Owl	42	Portsmouth NS	7. 2. 44	7. 5. 44	17. 7. 44 15. 11. 69		6/69 = AGSS-405		15. 11. 69	1951 FL Sn
406	Sea Poacher	42	Portsmouth NS	23. 2. 44	20. 5. 44	31. 7. 44		11/69 = AGSS-406 6/71 = SS-406	7/74 Peru	15. 8. 73	1952 G IA
407	Sea Robin	42	Portsmouth NS	1. 3. 44	25. 5. 44	7. 8. 44 1. 10. 70				1. 10. 70	1951 G IA
408	Sennet	42	Portsmouth NS	8. 3. 44	6. 6. 44	22. 8. 44 2. 12. 68				2. 12. 68	1952 FL Sn
409	Piper (ex-Awa)	42	Portsmouth NS	15. 3. 44	26. 6. 44	23. 8. 44 * 16. 6. 67		6/67 = AGSS-409		1. 7. 70	16. 6. 67 * 1. 7. 70 NRT 1951 FL Sn
410	Threadfin (ex-Sole)	42	Portsmouth NS	18. 3. 44	26. 6. 44	30. 8. 44 * 10. 12. 52			8/72 Turkey	1. 8. 73	7. 8. 53 * 18. 8. 72 1953 G IIA
411	Spadefish	42	Mare Island NS	27. 5. 43	8. 1. 44	9. 3. 44 3. 5. 46		12/62 = AGSS-411		1. 4. 67	
412	Trepang (ex-Senorita)	42	Mare Island NS	25. 6. 43	23. 3. 44	22. 5. 44 * 27. 6. 46		12/62 = AGSS-412		30. 6. 67	2. 60 * 30. 6. 67 NRT

Pennant number	Name	FY	Building yard	Keel laid	launched	commissioned / decommissioned	war (and other) loss	reclassified	transferred to	stricken	Remarks
413	*Spot*	42	Mare Island NS	24. 8. 43	19. 5. 44	3. 8. 44 * / 19. 6. 46			1/62 Chile		19. 8. 61 * / 12. 1. 62
414	*Springer*	42	Mare Island NS	30. 10. 43	3. 8. 44	18. 10. 44 * / 1. 47			1/61 Chile	1. 9. 72	24. 9. 60 * / 23. 1. 61
415	*Stickleback*	42	Mare Island NS	1. 3. 44	1. 1. 45	29. 3. 45 * / 26. 6. 46	(30. 5. 58)	6. 9. 51 * / 14. 11. 52 **		**	26. 6. 53
** 416	*Tiru*	42	Mare Island NS	17. 4. 44	16. 9. 47	1. 9. 48 / 1. 7. 75				1. 7. 75	1948 G II 1959 G III
425	*Trumpetfish*	42	Cramp	23. 8. 43	13. 5. 45	29. 1. 46 / 15. 10. 73			10/73 Brazil	15. 10. 73	1948 G II 1962 G III
426	*Tusk*	42	Cramp	23. 8. 43	8. 7. 45	11. 4. 46 / 18. 10. 73			10/73 Taiwan	18. 10. 73	1948 G II

Balao (SS-285), first of the 'thick-skinned' fleet submarines, seen here at the end of 1944 in Measure 32 camouflage and with a forward-mounted 5in deck gun. [USN]

Just over a year before her final decommissioning, *Balao* in the Mediterranean on 27 May 1962, with additional pennant number on her bows. [USN]

Crevalle (SS-291), with a rarely seen wealth of weaponry: two 5in L/25s and two 40mm AA guns. In this post-War photograph (1948) she has her pennant number painted in black on the bows. [AB]

Sablefish (SS-303) was delivered so late that she missed the War altogether; here she carries the standard armament but no 20mm AA guns. [AB]

Disarmed but still in camouflage, *Tilefish* (SS-307) is seen here in 1957, three years before being transferred to Venezuela. [USN]

Cabezon (SS-334) with armament removed, at Toulon in 1945, shortly after the end of the War. [MB]

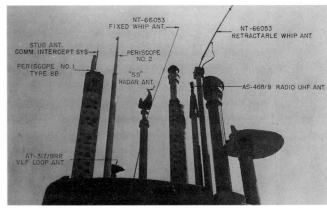

AS-371/S ANT.

AS-944/BLR ANT.

AT-693/BLR ANT.

NT-66053 WHIP ANT.

"ST" ANT.

AN/BPS-9 ANT.

T-66097 LOOP ANT.

NT-66053 FIXED WHIP ANT.

NT-66053 RETRACTABLE WHIP ANT.

STUB ANT. COMM. INTERCEPT SYS.

PERISCOPE NO. 2

PERISCOPE NO. I TYPE 8B

"SS" RADAR ANT.

AS-468/B RADIO UHF ANT.

AT-317/BRR V.L.F. LOOP ANT.

Ronquil (SS-396), 18 March 1960. Another Navy photograph showing details of conning tower fittings. [USN]

Close-up of the conning tower gear on *Mapiro* (SS-376), photographed on 12 September 1959, after reactivation work at the San Francisco Navy Yard. Note the small and therefore rarely seen ST radar antenna, mounted on one of the periscopes. [USN]

Undated photograph of *Hardhead* (SS-365), with forward-mounted 4in gun and unshielded 20mm AA gun. This must be one of the first examples of an SJ radar. [AB]

Capitaine, seen here off Hawaii as AGSS-336, which dates the photograph to between July 1960 and March 1966, when she was transferred to Italy. The JP hydrophone was also fitted to submarines in the 1960s. A performance award 'E' can be seen above the pennant number. [USN]

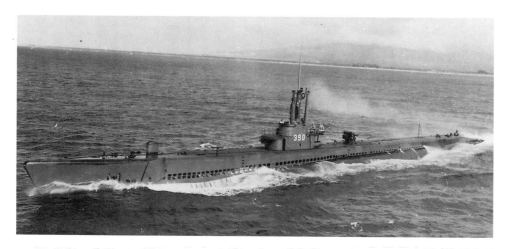

Plaice (SS-390), with pennant number in white. The photograph was probably taken not long before her first decommissioning, *circa* 1947. [AB]

Queenfish (SS-393), seen here in camouflage (*circa* 1959), remained in active service for a long time after the War. [AB]

▲
Sea Devil (AGSS-400), with no armament, 17 April 1963. [USN]

Spikefish (SS-404) entering Grand Harbour Valletta in Malta, 5 September 1955. [Pa]

Sea Robin (SS-407) at gunnery practice off the French Riviera, post-War. [MB]

Piper (SS-409) off Toulon, 1 May 1950. [MB]

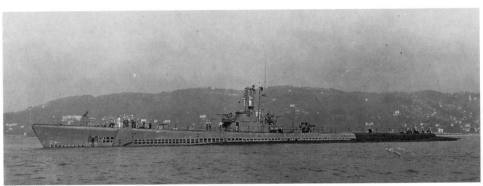

Detail of *Piper*'s conning tower, 15 May 1948. All horizontal surfaces and the upper parts of curved surfaces are painted black; 40mm AA guns are mounted on both cigarette decks. Lookouts stand on two tiny platforms each side of the periscope shears. The smaller radar antennae is an SS-2 and the larger probably an SV. [Halifax Herald Photo]

Threadfin (SS-410) post-War (1952), but still fully armed. [AB]

Spadefish (ex-AGSS-411) at Groton in 1968, about one year after having been stricken. [LvG]

Tench Class (SS-417)

Leaving aside the wartime modifications to the conning tower, there was no external difference between these boats and the two previous classes, or even the *Tambor* Class. What was new about the *Tench* Class was the layout of the fuel and ballast tanks. A new combined fuel trim tank was installed beneath the forward torpedo room to compensate weight changes brought about by discharged torpedoes and changes in stores stowage. Furthermore, the new torpedo-room layout allowed four more reloads to be carried. New, slower-running diesels with direct drive to the propller were installed, which made these boats considerably quieter. A good number of the later *Balao* submarines were actually allocated to the *Tench* Class.

As most of the *Tench* boats were commissioned at the end of the War, they did not see action. They were, however, candidates for the GUPPY and Fleet Snorkel modernization programmes.

Tench Class

Pennant numbers SS	Ships in the class		displacement surfaced submerged	Dimensions m			Output HP	Speed kn	Range Sm/kn	Oil fuel ts	Complement Officers/ enlisted	Original combat systems
	plan- ned	com- pleted		length	beam	draught						
417 – 424 435 475 – 490 522 – 525 suspen- diert: 436 – 437 438 – 474 491 492 – 517 518 – 521 526 – 562	136	29	1980–2000 2415	95,1 Operating depth 122 m	8,3	4,7	5400 2740	20,25 8,75	$11\,000_{10}$ 48 Std.$_{-2}$ endurance 75 days	430	10/71	1 to 2 - 5in L/25 6 bow, 4 stern TR 21in (28 Torpedoes, or 2 mines replacing 1 torpedo up to 40 max)

Powerplant: (a) 2 main and 1 auxiliary diesel operating 2 generators; (b) 2 electric motors driving propeller direct.

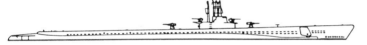

Tench Class.

Toro (SS-422), still armed and camouflaged, photographed off Toulon, 30 May 1953. [MB]

Toro again, about two years later, without armament. [USN]

Pennant number	Name	FY	Building yard	Keel laid	launched	commissioned / decommissioned	war (and other) loss	reclassified	transferred to	stricken	Remarks
417	Tench	42	Portsmouth NS	1. 4. 44	7. 7. 44	6. 10. 44 * / 1. 47		10/69 = AGSS-417 6/71 = SS-417		15. 8. 73	10. 50 * 8. 5. 70 1951 G IA
418	Thornback	42	Portsmouth NS	5. 4. 44	7. 7. 44	13. 10. 44 / 6. 4. 46 *			7/71 Turkey	1. 8. 73	2. 10. 53 * 1. 7. 71 1953 G IIA
419	Tigrone	42	Portsmouth NS	8. 5. 44	20. 7. 44	25. 10. 44 */ 1. 47	7. 48 ** 10. 57	4/48 = SSR-419 3/61 = SS-419 12/63 = AGSS-419		27. 6. 75	10. 3. 62 ** 27. 6. 75
420	Tirante	42	Portsmouth NS	28. 4. 44	9. 8. 44	6. 11. 44 / 20. 7. 46 *				1. 10. 73	26. 11. 52 * 1. 10. 73 1953 G IIA
421	Trutta (ex-Tomatate)	42	Portsmouth NS	22. 5. 44	18. 8. 44	16. 11. 44 */ 1947	1. 3.51 ** 14. 5. 52		7/72 Turkey	1. 7. 72	2. 1. 53 ** 1. 7. 72 1953 G IIA
422	Toro	42	Portsmouth NS	27. 5. 44	23. 8. 44	8. 12. 44 / 2. 2. 46 *		7/62 = AGSS-422		1. 4. 63	13. 5. 47 11. 3. 63
423	Torsk	42	Portsmouth NS	7. 6. 44	6. 9. 44	16. 12. 44 / 4. 3. 68 *		5/68 = AGSS-423 6/71 = IXSS-423		15. 12. 71	4. 3. 68 15. 12. 71 NRT 1952 FL Sn
424	Quillback (ex-Trembler)	42	Portsmouth NS	27. 6. 44	1. 10. 44	29. 12. 44 */ 4. 52				23. 3. 73	27. 2. 53 23. 3. 73 1953 G IIA
435	Corsair	43	Electric Boat	1. 3. 45	3. 5. 46	8. 11. 46 / 1. 2. 63		4/60 = AGSS-435		1. 2. 63	
475	Argonaut	43	Portsmouth NS	28. 6. 44	1. 10. 44	15. 1. 45 / 2. 12. 68			12/68 Canada	2. 12. 68	1952 FL Sn
476	Runner	43	Portsmouth NS	10. 7. 44	17. 10. 44	6. 2. 45 / 29. 6. 70 *		2/69 = AGSS-476 6/71 = IXSS-476		15. 12. 71	29. 6. 70 15. 12. 71 NRT 1952 FL Sn
477	Conger	43	Portsmouth NS	11. 7. 44	17. 10. 44	14. 2. 45 / 29. 7. 63		3/62 = AGSS-477		1. 8. 63	

Pennant number	Name	FY	Building yard	Keel laid	launched	commissioned / decommissioned	war (and other) loss	reclassified	transferred to	stricken	Remarks
478	*Cutlass*	43	Portsmouth NS	22. 7. 44	5. 11. 44	17. 3. 45 / 12. 4. 73			4/73 Taiwan	12. 4. 73	1948 G II
479	*Diablo*	43	Portsmouth NS	11. 8. 44	1. 12. 44	31. 3. 45 / 1. 6. 64	(4. 12. 71)	7/62 = AGSS-479	6/64 Pakistan		1964 FL Sn
480	*Medregal*	43	Portsmouth NS	21. 8. 44	15. 12. 44	14. 4. 45 / 1. 8. 70		5/67 = AGSS-480 10/69 = SS-480		1. 8. 70	1952 FL Sn
481	*Requin*	43	Portsmouth NS	24. 8. 44	1. 1. 45	28. 4. 45* / 3. 12. 68		1/48 = SSR-481 8/59 = SS-481 6/68 = AGSS-481 6/71 = IXSS-481		20. 12. 71	* 2. 69 20. 12. 71 NRT
482	*Irex*	43	Portsmouth NS	2. 10. 44	26. 1. 45	14. 5. 45 / 17. 11. 69		6/62 = AGSS-482		17. 11. 69	1947 FL Sn
483	*Sea Leopard*	43	Portsmouth NS	7. 11. 44	2. 3. 45	11. 6. 45 / 27. 3. 73			3/73 Brazil	27. 3. 73	1949 G II
484	*Odax*	43	Portsmouth NS	4. 12. 44	10. 4. 45	11. 7. 45 / 8. 7. 72			7/72 Brazil	8. 7. 72	1947 G I 1951 G II
485	*Sirago*	43	Portsmouth NS	3. 1. 45	11. 5. 45	13. 8. 45 / 1. 6. 72				1. 6. 72	1949 G II
486	*Pomodon*	43	Portsmouth NS	29. 1. 45	12. 6. 45	11. 9. 45 / 1. 4. 55*				1. 8. 70	* 2. 7. 55 1. 8. 70 1947 G I 1951 G II
487	*Remora*	43	Portsmouth NS	5. 3. 45	12. 7. 45	3. 1. 46 / 29. 10. 73			10/73 Greece	29. 10. 73	1947 G II 1962 G III
488	*Sarda*	43	Portsmouth NS	12. 4. 45	24. 8. 45	19. 4. 46 / 1. 6. 64		7/62 = AGSS-488		1. 6. 64	
489	*Spinax*	43	Portsmouth NS	14. 5. 45	20. 11. 45	20. 9. 46 / 11. 10. 69		1/48 = SSR-489 8/59 = SS-489 6/69 = AGSS-489		11. 10. 69	

Pennant number	Name	FY	Building yard	Keel laid	launched	commissioned / decommissioned	war (and other) loss	reclassified	transferred to	stricken	Remarks
490	*Volador*	43	Portsmouth NS	15. 6. 45	21. 5. 48	1. 10. 48 / 18. 8. 72			8/72 Italy	5. 12. 77	1948 G II / 1963 G III
522	*Amberjack*	43	Boston NS	8. 2. 44	15. 12. 44	4. 3. 46 / 17. 10. 73			10/73 Brazil	17. 10. 73	1947 G II
523	*Grampus*	43	Boston NS	8. 2. 44	15. 12. 44	26. 10. 49 / 13. 5. 72			5/72 Brazil	13. 5. 72	1950 G II
524	*Pickerel*	43	Boston NS	8. 2. 44	15. 12. 44	4. 4. 49 / 18. 8. 72			8/72 Italy	5. 12. 77	1949 G II / 1962 G III
525	*Grenadier*	43	Boston NS	8. 2. 44	15. 12. 44	10. 2. 51 / 15. 5. 73			5/73 Venezuela	15. 7. 73	1951 G II

Nine years after the taking of the photograph on p.105, *Toro* is seen in the Mediterranean on 27 August 1962, one month into her new career as AGSS-422. [MB]

Torsk (SS-423) off Toulon, 19 October 1950. [MB]

Eight months before her first decommissioning, *Quillback* (SS-424), still with full armament, photographed off Toulon, 18 August 1951. [MB]

Ten years later *Corsair* is now AGSS-435 and is painted black, 7 February 1962. [MB]

Cutlass (SS-478) in the Hudson River, New York, October 1945. [LvG]

Corsair (SS-435) without armament, 21 April 1952. The higher radar antenna is probably an SV, the lower an SS-2. The JP hydrophone is clearly visible on the foredeck. [USN]

Diablo (SS-479), wearing camouflage, 1956. [USN]

Five years later (9 September 1961)
Diablo painted black at Valletta,
Malta. Deck extensions for the former 5in gun mountings are clearly
visible. [Pa]

Sarda (SS-488) in 1954 with 40mm
AA guns temporarily removed. [USN]

Some two years afterwards (1956)
Sarda's anti-aircraft armament has
been reinstated. [AB]

1947-56: LATER CONVENTIONAL SUBMARINES

At the end of the Second World War, the US Navy had at its disposal a large number of what were for the time high-grade fleet submarines. It might have seemed that a stagnation point had been reached so far as further submarine design was concerned, but there was no chance of a breathing-space. The fundamental developments in submarine technology of the Type XXI U-boats had become known and were now the benchmark for all the major navies of the world. In particular, there were two parameters that now called into question earlier concepts of anti-submarine warfare by aircraft and surface vessels, and demanded new approaches. These parameters were

■ much higher underwater speeds as a result of improvements in battery design and the hydro-dynamics of the underwater hull-form
■ the advent of the snorkel and the resulting ability to remain submerged for much longer periods.

Access to this information was available to all the victorious Allies, not least to the specialists of the Soviet Navy. The rapidly deteriorating relationship between the Soviets and the West after the end of the War made it mandatory for the US Navy to find applications for this new technology in its own submarine fleet. This gave rise to the various GUPPY modernization programs described in the next section.

Obviously, these new trends also affected submarine classes under development, but the pace of change was so rapid that there was little time to put the ideas into effect. The one class that was built between 1951 and 1956 was the *Tang/Darter* Class. It appeared in the middle of all the GUPPY rebuilds, and was practically the last example of the conventional fleet submarine. In fact, in parallel with the realization of the *Tang* Class, the Navy was developing *Nautilus* (SSN-571), the first nuclear-powered submarine in the world. There were several new classes after the *Tang* Class, but each consisted of only a few special-purpose boats, such as hunter-killers, radar picket, training, target and test boats, and guided missile carriers. One particularly notable exception was the three-boat *Barbel* Class which, apart from its conventional powerplant, was built entirely to requirements that would soon be applied to nuclear submarines.

Tang Class (SS-563)

After the War, in Fiscal Year 1947, the US Navy began development of the first post-war submarine class, using the wartime experience of its own submarines. At the same time, it was possible to incorporate improvements that had been typical of the Type XXI U-boat introduced shortly before the end of the War, several examples of which had been captured by the Allies. The first notable thing about these boats was the dramatic improvement in underwater speed achieved by better batteries and a hydrodynamically improved hull form, and the second was the advantage of snorkel technology.

American submarines were plagued by problems with their diesels, so important for surface operations, and the *Tang* Class was no exception. Now, after five years of development, radial engine designs were still proving less than satisfactory. This type of cylinder layout – sometimes called the pancake layout because of its flat, circular appearance – was used in SS-563 to SS-566, whereas SS-567 and SS-568 reverted to a horizontal arrangement. Just five years after launching, the pancake diesels had to be replaced with in-line engines, which necessitated lengthening the hull by means of a 2.75-metre midships insertion. It should be noted, however, that the installed diesels took up about a third less space than the former engines, and were only half as heavy. During the 1960s, all six units were brought up to a standard length of 87.5 metres, to make room for additional electronic equipment as part of the FRAM (Fleet Rehabilitation and Modernization) program. The relatively short overall length of the *Tang* boats improved both speed and manoeuverability.

The design of these boats was the first to exclude deck armament, and there were fewer torpedo tubes than in the previous two classes. Although both sets of tubes were of the same diameter, they were of different lengths: the six bow tubes fired the standard, long torpedo, the four stern tubes being intended for the shorter, ASW torpedo.

Until the advent of the nuclear submarine, the *Tang*-boats were the USA's most highly developed submarines and not surprisingly, given the experimental atmosphere of their time, they were fitted with several different types of conning tower, as the photographs show. *Trigger*, for example, was one of several test-beds for the plastics sail used so extensively in later fleet submarine modernizations. In later phases, the stern torpedo tubes were no longer used, but all boats had the BQG-4 fire-control system installed, with its three distinctive shark-fin antennae mounted on deck at bows, stern and midships, directly aft of the sail.

Apart from the BQG-4 system, the most important electronic equipment was the BPS-12 radar and the BQR-3 and BQS-4 sonars. The BQG-4 system is designated Underwater Weapon System Mk 106 Mod 14.

Shortly after the completion of the *Tang* Class, the US Navy decided to build only nuclear submarines. With the exception of the *Darter* and *Barbel* Classes, conventional powerplant was only used for a few special-purpose vessels. These fast and well-equipped boats were however very attractive to medium-sized navies; thus SS-564 and SS-568 were transferred to Italy in 1973-4, while SS-565 to SS-567 were to have gone to Iran at the end of the 1970s, but with the fall of the Shah the transfer was cancelled. Between 1980 and 1983 SS-563 and SS-567 were transferred to Turkey. *Tang* and *Gudgeon* were reclassified as AGSS and SSAG respectively, and in April 1978 *Gudgeon* was assigned to acoustic test duties. The yard drawings for the *Tang* class, which up to the beginning of 1980 were still classified, are reproduced for interest as the endpapers to this book.

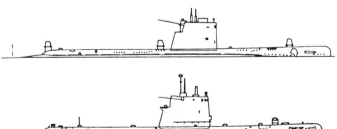

Wahoo with new sail and BQG-4 (PUFF) antenna.

Gudgeon in 1964, not yet fitted with the BQG system.

Tang Class

Pennant numbers	Ships in the class		displacement	Dimensions m			Output HP	Speed kn	Range Sm/kn	Oil fuel ts	Complement	Original combat systems
SS	planned	completed	surfaced submerged	length	beam	draught					Officers/ enlisted	
563 – 568	6	6	2050	82,1	8,3	5,2	4500	16	1988: surfaced 7600_{15} 14000_9 snorkelling	350	orig. 8/75	6 bow, 2 stern torpedo tubes 21in
			2260	length after extension 84,7, after further extension 87,5 m			5600	16 from other sources 20				
								17				

Diesel-electric drive; 3 diesels, 2 electric motors.

In this photograph dated 27 February 1961, *Tang* is seen with a new sail, probably of plastic. [USN]

Pennant number	Name	FY	Building yard	Keel laid	launched	commissioned / decommissioned	war (and other) loss	reclassified	transferred to	stricken	Remarks
563	*Tang*	47	Portsmouth NS	18. 4. 49	19. 6. 51	25. 10. 51 / 8. 2. 80		6/75 = AGSS-563	2/80 Turkey		
564	*Trigger*	47	Electric Boat	24. 2. 49	14. 6. 51	31. 3. 52 / 10. 7. 73			10/73 Italy	10. 7. 73	
565	*Wahoo*	48	Portsmouth NS	24. 10. 49	16. 10. 51	30. 5. 52 / 27. 6. 80				15. 7. 83	
566	*Trout*	48	Electric Boat	1. 12. 49	21. 8. 51	27. 6. 52 / 2. 1. 77				19. 12. 78	
567	*Gudgeon*	49	Portsmouth NS	20. 5. 50	11. 6. 52	21. 11. 52 / 30. 9. 83		4/78 = AGSS-567 11/79 = SSAG-567	9/83 Turkey	9. 83	
568	*Harder*	49	Electric Boat	30. 6. 50	3. 12. 51	19. 8. 52 / 20. 2. 74			2/74 Italy	20. 2. 74	

A special feature of the *Tang*-boats was the fact that they each had several different conning tower structures (later known as a 'sail') during the course of their service lives. The lead boat, *Tang* (SS-563), with her original conning tower, is seen off Portsmouth Navy Yard on 1 May 1952, some seven months after entering service. [USN]

Trigger (SS-564) with original conning tower, May 1952. [USN]

Ten years later (12 February 1962), *Trigger*, seen berthed in Genoa, has a different conning tower; the base is so wide that the deck has had to be extended. [AN]

This July 1966 aerial photograph of *Trigger* shows clearly the rounded form of the hull and conning tower designed to achieve greater underwater speed. [USN]

Trigger, in harbour at Valletta, Malta on 22 August 1966. [Pa]

Wahoo (SS-565) in 1960. [LvG]

Trout (SS-566) leaving Malta, 9 July 1964. [Pa]

Gudgeon (SS-567) was the longest-serving boat of this class. Taken near Hawaii on 3 January 1968, this photograph shows the shark-fin BQG-4 antennae. [USN] ▼

In June 1961 *Harder* (SS-568) attended Kiel's Navy Week celebrations. These two photographs show her leaving. [Te]

Harder with her final conning tower form, 1970. [USN]

Darter Class (SS-567)

The successor to the *Tang* Class, *Darter*, proved to be the only one of her kind, although at least three boats had been approved for 1954 and 1956. The lead boat should have been *Grayback* (SS-574), with *Growler* (SS-577) third, but they were re-allocated as guided missile submarines, leaving *Darter* the sole member of her class. She was designed along the same lines as the latter boats of the *Tang* class, but with some up-grading of materials. In 1965 *Darter* was lengthened by five metres, and her original diesels were replaced by improved models; however, Morison/Rowe is the only source that mentions this elongation. At the same time, it is probable that BQG-4 fire-control sonar was fitted as Underwater Weapons System Mk 106 Mod 11, as the three PUFF (Passive Underwater Fire-control Feasibility) antennae would seem to indicate.

One of *Darter*'s most important attributes was her silent running, attained through extensive sound-proofing in the machinery spaces. No further examples of this type were built because the diesel submarine had been made obsolete by high-speed teardrop hull forms and nuclear powerplant, and not because of deficiencies in *Darter*. In fact, she proved extremely useful as a training boat and, after 33 years' unbroken service with Sasebo, Japan, as her home port, was finally decommissioned in 1989. *Darter* shipped Mk 37 torpedoes only; replacement by Mk 48 was never scheduled.

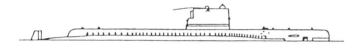

Darter, original appearance.

During her service with the Atlantic Fleet, *Darter* (SS-576) visited Genoa, where this photograph was taken on 30 June 1963. Note the folding 'cap-feather' antenna on the upper part of the conning tower. [GGh]

Darter Class

Pennant numbers	Ships in the class		displacement surfaced	Dimensions m			Output HP	Speed kn	Range Sm/kn	Oil fuel ts	Complement	Original combat systems
SS	planned	completed	submerged	length	beam	draught					Officers/enlisted	
576	1	1	1975	81,7	8,2	5,8	4500	16*			8/85	6 bow, 2 stern torpedo tubes 21in
			2250				4500	20				

3 diesel, 2 electric motors *
according to *Jane's* (1970-1) =
17/25KN ; according to Polmar 13
(1987) = 19.5/14KN

Darter was eventually transferred to the Pacific Fleet; here she is seen in Japanese waters off Maizuru in 1968. [LvG]

Pennant number	Name	FY	Building yard	Keel laid	launched	commissioned	war (and other) loss	reclassified	transferred to	stricken	Remarks
						decommissioned					
576	*Darter*	54	Electric Boat	10. 11. 54	28. 5. 56	20. 10. 56					
						89					

Barracuda (K-1) Class (SSK-1)

Soon after the end of the War, the US Navy decided to develop a medium-sized submarine, intended to locate and destroy enemy submarines under water. During construction, the boats were given, in addition to their official SSK pennant numbers the designations K-1 to K-3, but at the end of 1955 they were given traditional names beginning with 'B'. These boats were exceptionally quiet and their short hulls made them very manoeuvrable and thus highly suitable for anti-submarine operations. They were full of sonar and listening gear, and carried anti-submarine homing torpedoes.

Some years later, when the outstanding qualities of the nuclear-powered boats had become established, it was obvious that this design had been superseded. Range, speed and endurance were simply too low, and in 1959 the type was declared obsolete. After a relatively short service life, the SSK designation was dropped. *Bass* and *Bonita* were transferred to the reserve and later reclassified as SS-551 and SS-552, while *Barracuda* became a training boat in 1959, with the designation SST-3. Shortly before the end of her active service life she was again reclassified as SS-550. All three boats had their large bow sonar domes removed before decommissioning, *Barracuda*'s probably in about 1959.

Barracuda Class

Pennant numbers SSK	Ships in the class planned	Ships in the class completed	displacement surfaced submerged	Dimensions m length	beam	draught	Output HP	Speed kn	Range Sm/kn	Oil fuel ts	Complement Officers/enlisted	Original combat systems
1, 2, 3	3	3	765	59,8	7,6	4,9	1050	13			5/45	2 bow, 2 stern torpedo tubes 21in
			1160					13				

3 diesels, 2 electric motors.

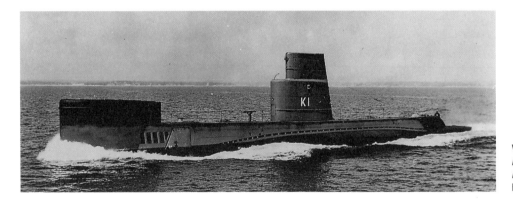

When this photograph was taken *Barracuda* was still known only as *K-1* (SSK-1). Note the old JP-type hydrophone. [USN]

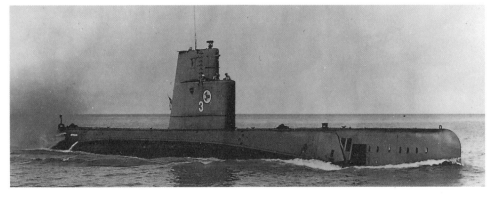

This photograph must have been taken after August 1959, because *Barracuda* has been reclassified SST-3 and her BQR-4 sonar dome has been removed. [USN]

Pennant number	Name	FY	Building yard	Keel laid	launched	commissioned / decommissioned	war (and other) loss	reclassified	transferred to	stricken	Remarks
SSK-1	*Barracuda* (ex-K-1)	48	Electric Boat	1. 7. 49	2. 3. 51	10. 11. 51 / 1. 10. 73		8/59 = SST-3 8/72 = SS-550		1. 10. 73	
SSK-2	*Bass* (ex-K-2)	48	Mare Island NS	23. 2. 50	2. 5. 51	16. 11. 52 / 1. 10. 57		8/59 = SS-551		1. 4. 65	
SSK-3	*Bonita* (ex-K-3)	49	Mare Island NS	19. 5. 50	21. 6. 51	11. 1. 52		8/59 = SS-552		1. 4. 65	

Bass (SSK-2), still with the huge bow-mounted BQR-4 sonar dome. [USN]

This photograph, taken off Mare Island on 11 February 1952, shows *Bonita* when she was still *K-3* (SSK-3); she was renamed three years later. [USN]

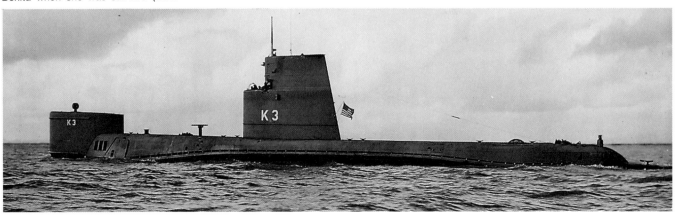

121

K-3 three months later. Photograph
dated 15 May 1952. [USN]

Mackerel (T-1) Class (SST-1)

These were the smallest submarines to have been
built by the US Navy for more than 40 years. From the
outset, both boats were designed for special duties.
The first was intended for training young submarine
officers, and for use as a target boat for surface and
aerial ASW warfare at the sonar training base at Key
West. The second was detailed for special duties at

various institutions. They were also used for testing
equipment and trying out submarine tactics.

Mackerel was originally intended to have the designation AGSS-570, but both boats were eventually
launched with the new designations SST-1 and
SST-2, the 'T' standing for 'target/training'. In mid-
1956, they were given the traditional names formerly
borne by SS-204 and SS-205. Building cost for each
boat was about $3 million.

Mackerel Class

Pennant numbers	Ships in the class		displacement surfaced	Dimensions m			Output HP	Speed kn	Range Sm/kn	Oil fuel ts	Comple- ment	Original combat systems
SST	plan- ned	com- pleted	submerged	length	beam	draught					Officers/ enlisted	
1, 2	2	2	303	40,0	4,2	3,7	1050	10	2000_{10}	18	2/16	1 bow torpedo tube 21in
			347					10				

2 diesels, 1 electric motor.

Pennant number	Name	FY	Building yard	Keel laid	launched	commissioned / decommissioned	war (and other) loss	reclassified	transferred to	stricken	Remarks
SST-1	*Mackerel* (ex-T-1)	51	Electric Boat	1. 4. 52	17. 7. 53	9. 10. 53 / 31. 1. 73				31. 1. 73	
SST-2	*Marlin* (ex-T-2)	52	Electric Boat	1. 5. 52	14. 10. 53	20. 11. 53 / 31. 1. 73				31. 1. 73	

Launch of *T-1* later *Mackerel*, at Electric Boat, Groton, 17 July 1953. She was almost complete at launching. [USN]

An undated photograph of *T-1* after completion. Note the BPS-series radar antenna and the almost universal hydrophone. [USN]

Marlin, then known only as *T-2* on 27 November 1953, seven days after commissioning. [USN]

Albacore Class (AGSS-569)

This was a single, special submarine for research on a radical new hull form and new types of propulsion plant. In the last phase of her development, she was far ahead of the submarine technology of her time, but at the expense of any fighting quality.

If one compares the hulls of submarines built before the nuclear age with its smooth, streamlined bodies of whales, sharks, dolphins or seals, the shape that will give better underwater performance is immediately apparent. The earlier submarine hulls had virtually no hydrodynamic shape at all. They were in effect surface ships able to travel under water, but only for as long as was necessary to avoid detection or attack, and their hulls were designed to be most effective on the surface. They were all edges and angles, which gave rise to under-water turbulence, as did the flat deck and the high-drag conning tower. Again, radar and sonar equipment caused as much turbulence as deck guns had done in the past. Boats with these characteristics could indeed only dive to avoid being seen by the enemy and, even then, their low under-water speed gave rise to serious tactical problems in trying to escape from or attack much faster surface ships. Then came the Type XXI U-boats, with their much improved under-water hull-form which was imitated by the US Navy's *Tang* Class.

With the introduction of *Albacore* at the end of 1953, submarine technology moved into a revolutionary new phase. The hull was of the 'teardrop' shape which all the streamlined marine creatures mentioned above possess, and it greatly improved underwater speed. On the other hand, it is clear from numerous photographs how poorly it is suited to surface operation. In particular, the strong wake arising from surface drag made it clearly visible at great distances.

Albacore was a revelation to the submarine fleet, not only because of the new hull form, but also because of other knowledge gained during the course of her 19-years' service life. One particularly useful aspect was the fact that she was rebuilt four times during a nine-year period, with improvements occurring at every phase.

■ Phase I (1953): cruciform stern

- Phase II (1956): open stern, plastics bow extension providing sonar window
- Phase III (1959): improved sonar, x-form tail fins, dive-brakes aft on sail
- Phase IV (1961): fully electric drive with contra-rotating propellers driven by coaxial shafts.

In 1963, heavy-duty silver-zinc batteries were introduced, as a result of which underwater speed reached 33 knots, which meant that she could outrun almost anything on the surface. The teardrop hull form was also used in the three *Barbel* – Class boats of 1956.

Albacore was decommissioned in 1972 and stricken in 1980, but was still in the care of the Naval Inactive Ships Maintenance Facility (NISMF) at the Navat Base in Philadelphia in 1984. At the end of the 1980s *Albacore* was preserved at Portsmouth, N.H.

Albacore, original appearance.

Pennant numbers	Ships in the class		displacement surfaced	Dimensions m			Output HP	Speed kn	Range Sm/kn	Oil fuel ts	Comple-ment	Original combat systems
AGSS	plan-ned	com-pleted	submerged	length	beam	draught					Officers/ enlisted	
569	1	1	1517	62,0	8,4	5,7	1700	25			5/47	–
			1847				15000	33				

2 diesels, 1 electric motor, varying.

Pen-nant num-ber	Name	FY	Building yard	Keel laid	launched	commis-sioned	war (and other) loss	reclas-sified	transferred to	stricken	Remarks
						decom-missioned					
AGSS-569	*Albacore*	50	Portsmouth NS	15. 3. 52	1. 8. 53	5. 12. 53				1. 5. 80	
						1. 9. 72					

Albacore (AGSS-569) in April 1954, during the first phase of her service life, seen here at high speed with her bow diving fins folded for surface running. [USN]

Three years after decommissioning, *Albacore* rests at the Naval Inactive Ships Maintenance Facility at Philadelphia, still sporting the x-shaped tail fins fitted in 1959. As a 'mothballed' vessel, like *Wahoo* behind her, she has ventilation equipment fitted to her conning tower to keep the interior at an even temperature and humidity. As *Wahoo* was mothballed in 1980, this photograph must have been taken since then. [LvG]

Another view of the NISMF at Philadelphia, 2 April 1984: twelve years after decommissioning, *Albacore* is still there. Her two companions are *Wahoo* (SS-565), with BQG-4 antennae, and *Trout* (SS-566), the other ship being the destroyer *Manley* (DD-940). [Te]

126

Sailfish Class (SSR-572)

The radar picket concept came into existence during the last phase of the Second World War. Put simply, it meant having destroyers (DDR) flanking a carrier group to give radar early warning of the approach of Japanese *kamikaze* aircraft. After the War, the conversion of more destroyers from DD to DDR designation indicated that this concept was being taken further. But as quite a number of destroyers had been lost or badly damaged during 1944-5, ten fleet submarines were converted for radar picket duties after the War ended.

The *Sailfish* Class was developed because the older SSR boats were simply too slow on the surface to keep up with fast carrier groups, although the design was intended to overcome other failings too. This was also the first time that a submarine had been designed specifically for radar early-warning duties. At the time they were delivered, the two *Sailfish* boats were the largest in the US Navy, apart from the old *Argonaut* (SM-1) and the three *Narwhal*s from the pre-War era.

At first, both units had BPS-2 and BPS-3 radars, one mounted on the deck directly astern of the sail, with an air-control centre inside the boat. After the abandonment of the radar-picket concept at the end of the 1950s, both boats were reclassified in March 1961 as standard fleet submarines, with consecutive 'SS' numbers. The air-control centre was converted to an operational control centre, and both radars were removed. Before she was reclassified, *Salmon* was equipped to control guided missiles, but very little information was ever published, just as there were no published photographs of the large radome she was supposed to have carried.

After no more than three years as fleet submarines, both units were modernized under the FRAM II program, although, in the *Dictionary of American Naval Fighting Ships*, this is inaccurately described as a GUPPY III conversion. *Sailfish* was the first to be modernized (1964-6), and then both boats received BQG-4 fire-control sonar and PUFF antennae. At about this time they carried out several patrols with the 6th Fleet in the Mediterranean. Then, from June 1968, *Salmon* was reclassified AGSS-573 for a period of a year, acting as mother-ship for Deep Submergence Rescue Vessels (DSRV) as part of the Submarine Rescue Program, when her PUFF antennae were removed. At the end of this time she returned to the fleet, once again under her original 'SS' designation. *Sailfish* was also classified AGSS for a one-year period.

Two sources (Silverstone, 1987 and Fahey, vol. VIII) refer to two torpedo tubes in this class. All other sources say they had six bow tubes, but apparently only twelve torpedoes were carried, despite the size of these boats. During post-FRAM operations, they were equipped with Mk 106 Mod 21 weapons-control systems and BQS-4 sonars.

Both boats managed to put in more than 20 years' service before being stricken in 1978. *Salmon* ended up as a target, but *Sailfish* was still in the Norfolk NISMF in 1988.

Sailfish Class

Pennant numbers	Ships in the class		displacement surfaced	Dimensions m			Output HP	Speed kn	Range Sm/kn	Oil fuel ts	Complement	Original combat systems
SSR	planned	completed	submerged	length	beam	draught					Officers/ enlisted	
572, 573	2	2	2625	106,8	8,8	5,0	6000	19,5			12/96	6 bow torpedo tube 21in
			3168				8200	10*				(12 Torpedoes)

4 diesels, 2 electric motors
*14 knots after removal of radars

Pennant number	Name	FY	Building yard	Keel laid	launched	commissioned / decommissioned	war (and other) loss	reclassified	transferred to	stricken	Remarks
SSR-572	*Sailfish*	52	Portsmouth NS	8. 12. 53	7. 9. 55	14. 4. 56		3/61 = SS-572 6/68 = AGSS-572*		30. 9. 78	* 6/69 = SS-572
SSR-573	*Salmon*	51	Portsmouth NS	10. 3. 54	25. 2. 56	25. 8. 56		3/61 = SS-573 6/68 = AGSS-573* 6/69 = SS-573		1. 10. 77	

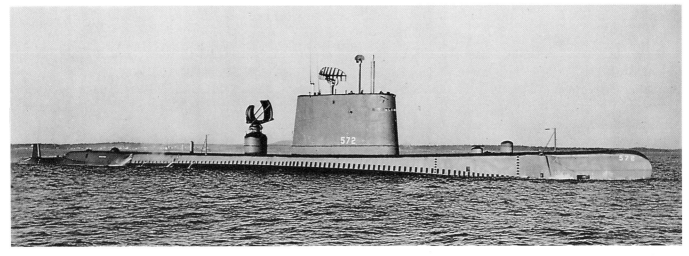

Sailfish (SSR-572), on 5 November 1956, seven months after commissioning. The large antenna on the sail indicates a BPS-2 radar (replacing the SR-2), and the deck antenna is for the BPS-3 air-search radar. [USN]

Sailfish in June 1966, after reclassification as 'SS', now with BQG-4 sonar (with PUFFs) but without large radar antennae. 2.66. [USN]

Sailfish, berthed at the Norfolk NISMF, 1 October 1988, ten years after being stricken. [Te]

A photograph of *Salmon* as SSR-573, 4 February 1957; only the BPS-3 radar antenna can be seen. [USN]

A Sea King SH-3A sub-hunter overflies *Salmon* during a training exercise off the southern California coast, 21 January 1976. [USN]

Grayback Class (SSG-574)

As we have noted previously, these two boats were originally intended to be the other members of the class of which Darter (SS-576) was the third. However, this was the beginning of the era of the seaborne guided missile, and it was realized that they could also be installed on submarines. In 1956, therefore, Grayback and Growler (replacing the older SSGs Tunny and Perch) were re-allocated as guided-missile submarines (SSG), to be armed with the Regulus II missile which was at that time under development. The original 'SS' designations were therefore amended to SSG-574 and SSG-577 respectively.

The original intention had been that each SSG would carry two Regulus II cruise missiles in twin hangars on the foredeck. However, the Regulus program was suspended in favour of the Polaris ballistic missile program, and so in 1964 both boats were equipped to carry four of the older Regulus I missiles without loss of attack capacity. The range of the cancelled Regulus II had been intended to be 1,000 miles, double the 500-mile range of Regulus I.

When the Regulus I programme was also cancelled, Grayback underwent a lengthy conversion to transport submarine, which took five years in all. She was then equipped to carry 85 commandos with rubber boats and full equipment for seaborne assaults. It had also been planned to rebuild Growler, but when the cost of converting Grayback came out at $30M, twice the budgeted sum, this was cancelled in 1968 and Growler was transferred to the reserve without further operational service. According to Jane's, 1969-70, Grayback was never officially classified APSS, but was in fact LPSS, whereas Musgrove, vol. I, gives the APSS designation. Several sources note the reclassification of Growler at the end of her active service, but Musgrove disputes this. Grayback was reclassified SS-574 in June 1975, and served in the western Pacific where her amphibious transport capability was maintained until her decommissioning in 1984.

Preparation of these vessels for their guided-missile function saw the original Darter-type hull cut in half and a 15-metre section welded in place. The foreship was strengthened to take the weight of the twin Regulus hangars. The LPSS rebuild was funded in Fiscal Year 1965, and the Regulus hangars were then reconstructed as equipment shelters for the embarked assault unit. In addition to the BQS-4 sonar already fitted, BQG-4 was installed, as evidenced by the PUFF antennae. None of this applied to Growler. Before the LPSS rebuild, Grayback had a noticeably higher conning tower than Growler.

Grayback Class

Pennant numbers	Ships in the class		displacement surfaced	Dimensions m			Output HP	Speed kn	Range Sm/kn	Oil fuel ts	Complement	Original combat systems
SSG	planned	completed	submerged	length	beam	draught					Officers/ enlisted	
574, 577	2	2	574: 2670	574: 98,3	9,1	5,8	4500	20			9/87	6 bow, 2 stern torpedo tubes 21in
			3650 577: 2540	574 as LPSS: 101,8	9,0	5,8	5600	17			as LPSS: 10/78 +10/75 troops	4 Regulus I guided missiles
			3515	577: only 96,8	8,3	5,8						

3 diesels, 2 electric motors

Pennant number	Name	FY	Building yard	Keel laid	launched	commissioned / decommissioned	war (and other) loss	reclassified	transferred to	stricken	Remarks
SSG-574	*Grayback*	52	Mare Island NS	1. 7. 54	2. 7. 57	7. 3. 58 / 25. 5. 64		8/68 = APSS-574 1/69 = LPSS-574 6/75 = SS-574		15. 1. 84	9. 5. 69 / 16. 1. 84
SSG-577	*Growler*	55	Portsmouth NS	15. 2. 55	5. 4. 57	30. 8. 58 / 25. 5. 64				1. 8. 80	

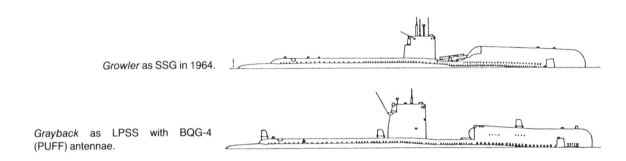

Growler as SSG in 1964.

Grayback as LPSS with BQG-4 (PUFF) antennae.

Commissioning of *Grayback* as SSG-574, 7 March 1958. A Regulus I can be seen on the launch ramp. [USN]

Grayback as SS-574 on 18 August 1982 in Maizuru Bay, Japan, with both hangar doors open. It is not unusual for submarines to be without visible identification number even in peacetime. [TH]

Although this photograph of *Grayback* is undated, the presence of BQG-4 antennae means that it must have been taken after the APSS conversion. [USN]

Barbel Class (SS-580)

This was the last series of (three) conventionally-powered American submarines, but it was also the first class to use the teardrop hull form pioneered by *Albacore*. It therefore marked a milestone on the road to nuclear submarines and streamlined hulls, although there would be some variations in the later SSN classes. However, the new hull form gave these boats a dramatic increase in speed.

Initially, the diving planes were located forward, but later – and this was another trend to be continued in the nuclear boats – they were fitted near the leading edge of the sail structure. The trend was reversed in the later *SSN-688*-Class boats, when the planes were relocated at the bow. This is also the case in the new *Seawolf* Class.

Modern, Mk 48 torpedoes could be launched from six bow tubes, and the boats were equipped with BPS-12 radar and BQR-2 and SQS-49 sonars, as well as a WLR-1 ECCM unit and a Mk 101 Mod 20 weapons-control system. Overall, they have been described as having been outstandingly successful. During their later years, they served in the Pacific as decoys in Soviet submarine simulation exercises. *Bonefish* was, in 1982, the only diesel submarine serving in the Atlantic. At the end of April 1988 an explosion in the battery room left three crew members dead and 22 suffering the effects of smoke inhalation; she was taken out of service at the end of the year without having been repaired. The remaining two boats were decommissioned in 1990 after 30 years' service.

Barbel Class

Pennant numbers	Ships in the class		displacement surfaced	Dimensions m			Output HP	Speed kn	Range Sm/kn	Oil fuel ts	Comple- ment	Original combat systems
SS	plan- ned	com- pleted	submerged	length	beam	draught					Officers/ enlisted	
580 – 582	3	3	2146	66,8	8,8	8,5	4800	15			8/77	6 bow torpedo tubes 21in
			2640				3150	25				

3 diesels, 2 electric motors

Barbel Class

Pennant number	Name	FY	Building yard	Keel laid	launched	commis- sioned	war (and other) loss	reclas- sified	transferred to	stricken	Remarks
						decom- missioned					
SS- 580	*Barbel*	56	Portsmouth NS	18. 5. 56	19. 7. 58	17. 1. 59					
						90					
SS- 581	*Blueback*	56	Ingalls	15. 4. 57	16. 5. 59	15. 10. 59					
						90					
SS- 582	*Bonefish*	56	New York S.B.	3. 6. 57	22. 11. 58	9. 7. 59					
						28. 9. 88					

Original appearance of *Barbel* (SS-580), seen here in 1960 at high speed on the surface with periscopes and antennae extended. The diving fins were located on the hull at this time. [USN]

Blueback (SS-581) after relocation of diving fins on the sail structure. [SoW]

Bonefish (SS-582), photographed during a visit to Hamburg. [RNe]

Dolphin Class (AGSS-555)

The relatively low pennant number of *Dolphin* is explained by the fact that about seven years elapsed between authorization and commissioning. When she was finally delivered, the Navy was already operating nuclear submarines with pennant numbers about 100 higher. This was of course due to the mass delivery of the strategic ballistic-missile submarine (SSBN) in the mid-1960s. *Dolphin* was one of two conventionally powered AGSS boats, intended for use as research vessels. The first, *Albacore*, was to be used to test hull form as well as powerplant and equipment; *Dolphin* would carry out deep-diving tests with an eye to the coming generation of SSN and SSBN boats, and their submerged performance. Since this depended pri-

marily on the quality of steel used, *Dolphin*'s design objective was to investigate the various possibilities.

The hull form was cylindrical, capped at both ends and made of high-tensile steel. The actual operating depth achieved is of course classified, but it is known that *Dolphin* could operate deeper than any other naval submarine of her time, which means certainly in excess of 400 metres. She was also used for acoustic and oceanographic research; some time after 1970 the only bow torpedo tube was removed to provide space for an extra twelve tons of scientific equipment.

In addition to her deep-diving capability, *Dolphin* was extremely silent. Tests of several different battery types were carried out, and, from what one can glean from the literature, it would seem that under-water speed could be increased by 10 or even 15 knots depending on the type of battery used. Apart from the acoustic research equipment in the foreship, *Dolphin* carried BQR-2 sonar and a variable-depth sonar array (VDS) with more than 1,200 metres of towing cable. Surface navigation was carried out using SPS-53 radar, which can be removed if necessary. Also, a new type of rudder made the hitherto obligatory diving planes redundant, so that built-in safety systems had to be incorporated to ensure that the submarine could self-surface in the event of an accident.

Dolphin is assigned to Submarine Development Group 1 in San Diego. At the Ballast Point submarine base, her low profile is such that she has seldom been photographed.

Dolphin Class

Pennant numbers AGSS	Ships in the class		displacement surfaced submerged	Dimensions m			Output HP	Speed kn	Range Sm/kn	Oil fuel ts	Comple- ment Officers/ enlisted	Original combat systems
	plan- ned	com- pleted		length	beam	draught						
555	1	1	860	50,3	5,9	4,9	1650	7,5	endurance 14 days		4/26 + 5	1 21in bow torpedo tube, removed 1970
			950					15				
									12 Std.			

2 diesels, 1 electric motor

Dolphin (AGSS-555) on the day of her launch, 6 August 1968. [USN]

Pennant number	Name	FY	Building yard	Keel laid	launched	commissioned / decommissioned	war (and other) loss	reclassified	transferred to	stricken	Remarks
AGSS-555	*Dolphin*	61	Portsmouth NS	9. 11. 62	8. 6. 68	17. 8. 68					1989 reactivated

Shortly after commissioning, *Dolphin* is seen on sea trials off Portsmouth Navy Yard, 21 November 1968. [USN]

Dolphin's commissioning, 17 August 1968 – but quite some time was to elapse before she was eventually ready for action. [USN]

1947-64: FLEET SUBMARINE CONVERSIONS

At the end of the War the victorious Western Allies took possession of a number of unfinished Type XXI U-boats. In many ways these heralded a new era in submarine construction. Their submerged speed was such that they could outrun surface attackers and, with the recently developed snorkel, could stay submerged for long periods, using their diesels for battery recharging. The advantages of the Walter closed-circuit hydrogen peroxide turbine had not been available to the Germans because it had not been fully developed by the end of the War. Even so, the advances embodied in the Type XXI were so revolutionary that all the Great Powers had to think again about submarine design.

Since the Soviets had also got hold of several examples of the Type XXI, the Americans realized that technological changes would be required not only in submarines, but in ASW surface vessels also. They felt that there was not much point in having large numbers of fast new submarines if these did not embody the leading edge of current technology. The American submarine fleet therefore had to be renewed after 1945, and this took place in two very unequal ways. The direct descendants of the Type XXI U-Boats were the seven boats of the *Tang* and *Darter* Classes, while the Soviet Navy built large numbers of boats of the much bigger W-Class. The reason why the Americans built so few conventionally powered fleet submarines after the War were:

■ the large number of existing fleet submarines capable of being converted;
■ the early post-War indications of the advent of nuclear power for submarines, and the attention this new technology attracted.

The first task the Navy had to address, with submarines as with surface ships, was the bringing of the fleet up to a minimum peacetime condition. This was done in the following ways:

■ the old boats of the O-, R- and S-Classes, together with the V-boats, were scrapped immediately after the War, as were newer boats that had been damaged beyond economic repair;
■ the slightly newer P- and S-boats, plus the *Tambor*-Class with its shallow, 75-metre operating depth, were no longer viable, and many were written off as training hulks;
■ the 'thin-skinned' boats of the *Gato* Class were also unsuitable for modern conditions and all but six of them, plus nearly fifty per cent of the *Balao* boats, were transferred to the Reserve Fleet and mothballed within three years of the end of the War.

Before the vessels were mothballed all batteries were removed for factory reconditioning and new or reconditioned batteries were installed. There were three locations for mothballed submarines: New London, Connecticut; Philadelphia, Pennsylvania; and Mare Island, California. In summary, the disposal of fleet submarines after the War was:

■ 20 scrapped
■ 19 converted to training hulks
■ 106 transferred to reserve
■ 4 unfinished hulks set aside for completion later.

The shipbuilding industry, too, underwent a peace-time transformation. The Cramp and Manitowoc yards, plus the Boston Navy Yard, were taken off submarine construction, leaving both design and building concentrated at Portsmouth, Mare Island and Electric Boat. Terminology was also changed: the former designation 'Navy Yard' was replaced with 'Naval Shipyard', as this was felt to be more in tune with the times.

Also in tune with the times, of course, was nuclear weapons testing in the Pacific, and in particular the important tests carried out in July 1946 to determine the effect of nuclear explosions on various ship types, including submarines. The results on the eight boats used as surface and submerged targets showed that damage was considerably less than had originally been feared. Indeed, several boats, after decontamination, were capable of surface running under their own power. The boats used in these tests were: *Skipjack* (SS-184), *Searaven* (SS-196), *Tuna* (SS-203), *Skate* (SS-305), *Apogon* (SS-308), *Dentuda* (SS-335), *Parche* (SS-384) and *Pilotfish* (SS-386).*

In parallel with the situation described above, came the application of the new technology to the existing submarine fleet. As a result, many of these boats were given new designations after reconstruction, to represent the many new purposes for which they were intended. Some indication of the great versatility of the submarine can be had if one considers that the following categories were used at various times:

- SSA (later ASSA): cargo submarine
- SSG: guided-missile submarine
- SSK: anti-submarine submarine (killer)
- SSO (later AOSS): submarine oiler (tanker)
- SSP (later ASSP, APSS, or LPSS): submarine, transport
- SSR: radar picket submarine
- SST: target and training submarine
- AGSS: auxiliary submarine
- IXSS (from 1971): administrative classification for training hulks.

The individual rebuilds are described in the following pages.

Shipyards

The shipyards involved in the various fleet submarine reconstruction programs are referred to by the following abbreviations:

Pts   Portsmouth Naval Shipyard
MI   Mare Island Naval Shipyard
EB   Electric Boat
Phil   Philadelphia Naval Shipyard
Bos   Boston Naval Shipyard
SF   San Francisco Naval Shipyard
Chas   Charleston Naval Shipyard
Pearl   Pearl Harbor Naval Shipyard

GUPPY Conversions

GUPPY I Conversions

Immediately after the end of the Second World War the US Navy began a program of modernization of its many existing submarines using captured German technology. In particular, the objective was to obtain greater submerged power and performance for the wartime fleet submarine classes, for which reason the program was given the acronym GUPPY (Greater Underwater Propulsive Power). The start of what was to become a multi-faceted program was the conversion of two units to the GUPPY I model, for use as ASW training boats. The rebuilding was done quickly, in 1947, when the US Navy still had no available snorkels. The excellent results of the rebuild were due to the following four factors:

- streamlining the hull
- streamlining the conning tower, the upper extension of which carried only one periscope and one radar antenna
- doubling battery capacity
- extensive interior redesign to accommodate the additional batteries.

The particular form of conning tower arrived at for

* For more information on these tests, see the Author's article 'Vor 31 Jahren: Atombombversuche der US Navy Bikini' (31 Years Ago: US Navy Nuclear Tests at Bikini) in the journal *Marine Rundschau*, No 11, 1977.

this design was never exactly copied in succeeding models. Four years after this first rebuild, both units were advanced to the GUPPY II Program, which meant, among other things, the addition of a snorkel and the removal of the diesel connected to the auxiliary generator.

The GUPPY I Program

PN	Name	Original Class	In Service	Shipyard	Conversion Complete
484	*Odax*	Tench	45	Pts	47
486	*Pomodon*	Tench	45	MI	47

Model GUPPY I Conversion

Pennant numbers SS	Ships in the class planned	Ships in the class completed	displacement surfaced submerged	Dimensions m length	beam	draught	Output HP	Speed kn	Range Sm/kn	Oil fuel ts	Complement Officers/ enlisted	Original combat systems
484, 486	2 aus FY 47	2	1990 2400	93,8	8,3		4610	17,8 18,2			10/69	6 bow, 4 stern Torpedo Tubes 21in

Powerplant: as *Tench* Class, but less
1 generator diesel; four 126-cell
batteries.

GUPPY I conversion.

GUPPY I rebuild: some of the radical changes which gave additional submerged speed to the conventional fleet submarines can be seen in this photograph, taken after conversion, of *Odax* (SS-484), the first GUPPY I conversion. Note the streamlined hull and conning tower. She is seen off Portsmouth, NH on 11 July 1947. [USN]

Pomodon (SS-486), the second GUPPY I rebuild.

The GUPPY II Program

PN	Name	Original-Class	In Service	Shipyard	Conver-sion Complete
339	*Catfish*	Balao	45	MI	49
343	*Clamagore*	Balao	45	EB	48
344	*Cobbler*	Balao	45	EB	49
345	*Cochino*	Balao	45	EB	49
346	*Corporal*	Balao	45	EB	48
347	*Cubera*	Balao	45	Phil	48
349	*Diodon*	Balao	46	MI	48
350	*Dogfish*	Balao	46	Phil	48
351	*Greenfish*	Balao	46	Pts	48
352	*Halfbeak*	Balao	46	EB	48
416	*Tiru*	Balao	–	MI	48
425	*Trumpetfish*	Balao	46	Pts	48
426	*Tusk*	Balao	46	Pts	48
478	*Cutlas*	Tench	45	Phil	48
483	*Sea Leopard*	Tench	45	Phil	49
484	*Odax*	aus Guppy I		Pts	51
485	*Sirago*	Tench	45	Phil	49
486	*Pomodon*	aus Guppy I		MI	51
487	*Remora*	Tench	46	MI	47
490	*Volador*	Tench	–	Pts	48
522	*Amberjack*	Tench	46	Pts	47
523	*Grampus*	Tench	–	Bos	50
524	*Pickerel*	Tench	–	Pts	49
525	*Grenadier*	Tench	–	Bos	51

GUPPY II Conversions

The GUPPY II Program followed soon after the end of the first rebuilds, and involved 24 boats of the *Balao* and *Tench* Classes, plus both GUPPY I boats. Interior re-arrangement gave problems similar to those of the GUPPY I rebuild. Typical improvements in this second program included the provision of a snorkel and yet another conning tower redesign. For GUPPY II and the remainder of the GUPPY program, design work was carried out only by the Portsmouth Naval Shipyard and the privately owned Electric Boat Company. There were some differences between the two in interior design and, notably, in the conning tower. These differences disappeared later in the program, when many boats were fitted with taller, more corrosion-resistant plastics sails. Several boats that had been unfinished at the end of the War – SS-416, SS-490, SS-523, SS-524 and SS-525 – were transferred direct to the GUPPY II program.

Model GUPPY II Conversions

Pennant numbers SS	Ships in the class		displacement surfaced submerged	Dimensions m			Output HP	Speed kn	Range Sm/kn	Oil fuel ts	Comple- ment Officers/ enlisted	Original combat systems
	plan- ned	com- pleted		length	beam	draught						
339 343 – 347 349 – 352 416, 425 426, 478 483 – 487 490 522 – 525	24 aus FY 48 – FY 50	24	2040 2400 bis 2075 2420	93,6	8,3		4610	18 16			~ 10/75	6 bow, 4 stern Topedo tubes 21in

Powerplant: some units – direct
diesel-electric after removal of
gearing; four 126-cell batteries.

GUPPY II rebuild with Portsmouth
conning tower.

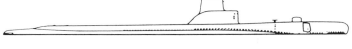

GUPPY II rebuild with Electric Boat
conning tower.

Cobbler as a GUPPY II rebuild.

GUPPY II rebuild with plastics sail.

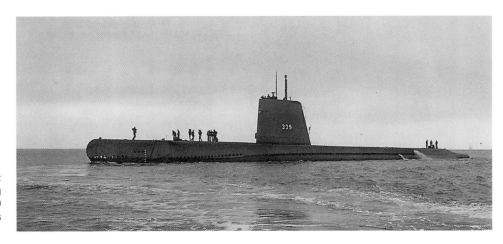

Seventeen years as a GUPPY II:
Catfish (SS-339), seen here during
the last years of her service life (19
August 1966), fitted with a plastics
sail. [USN]

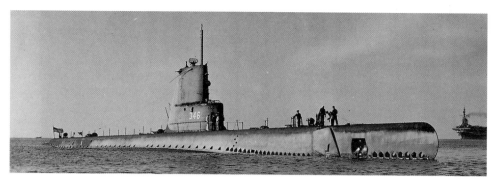

Corporal (SS-346), a GUPPY II with the Electric Boat-type conning tower, photographed on 24 September 1952. The SV radar antenna is aft of the periscope, and the horizontal surfaces appear to be wearing (deliberately?) uneven dark camouflage. [MB]

▲
Black-painted *Diodon* (SS-349), after her refit at San Francisco Naval Shipyard, photographed on 22 October 1957 off Hunter's Point. [USN]

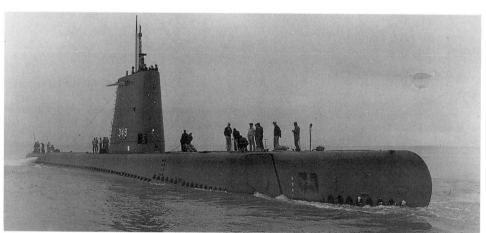

A later shot (30 August 1965) of *Diodon*, not with plastics sail. [USN]

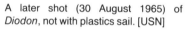

Dogfish (SS-350), off the French Riviera, 5 February 1965. [USN]

Beam shot of *Halfbeak* (SS-352); note the sonar dome forward of the conning tower. [AB]

Official Navy photograph (21 January 1960) of the various fittings to *Diodon*'s conning tower, by this time probably already a plastics sail structure. [USN]

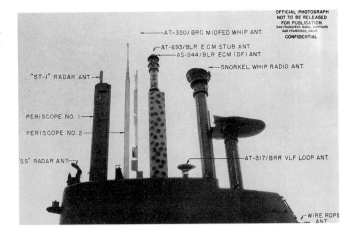

Trumpetfish (SS-425), a *Balao*-type GUPPY II. From this angle the conning tower resembles those of the GUPPY I boats. [AB]

Tusk (SS-426) seen on 1 August 1952, with Portsmouth-type conning tower and SV radar, plus deck-mounted sonar dome and hydrophone. [USN]

Fifteen years later (May 1967): *Tusk*, now with plastics sail, photographed off New York. [USN]

Tusk in 1972, shortly before her transfer to Taiwan. The height and width of the plastics sail are very evident. [AB]

◄ Philadelphia GUPPY rebuilds used the Portsmouth-type conning tower. Here we see an example in *Sea Leopard* (SS-483), photographed off Toulon, 19 October 1950. [MB]

Undated photograph of the first GUPPY I boat, *Odax* (SS-484), after her GUPPY II rebuild. The 'cap-feather'-type radio antenna can be seen on top of the sail structure. [USN] ▼

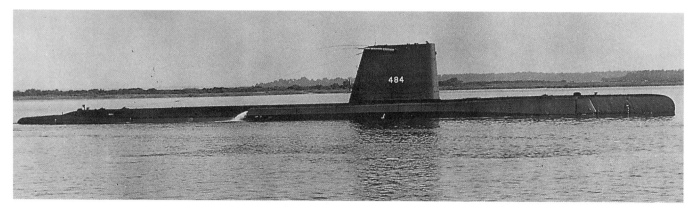

Detail of the later plastics sail as fitted to *Sea Leopard*, with SS-2 radar antenna, 18 July 1971. The patch where the pennant number has been painted out is clearly visible. [LG])

Sirago (SS-485) without pennant number, seen off Philadelphia Naval Shipyard on 27 July 1949, soon after GUPPY II conversion. [USN]

More than two years later (24 October 1951): *Sirago* off Toulon, with bow sonar dome. [MB]

A last look at *Pomodon* (SS-486), 24 April 1961, the second of the GUPPY I units, which was also converted in the GUPPY II program [USN] ▼

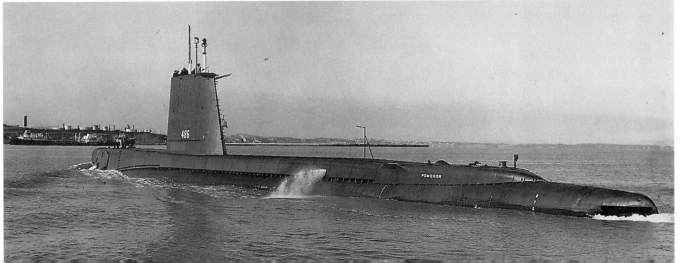

Remora (SS-487), one of the boats later modernized in the FRAM II (GUPPY III) program. [USN]

Volador (SS-490), with a torpedo stuck in her 'vest pocket' after an exercise. [USN]

Grampus (SS-523), 3 June 1964. [MB]

Pickerel (SS-524) off Pearl Harbor, with all gear extended, 4 April 1955. [USN] ▼

GUPPY IA Conversions

The US Navy has always had problems with funding, and this was the case even at the end of the Second World War. The GUPPY II program proved extremely expensive and more cost-effective solutions had to be found. This requirement resulted in the GUPPY IA and GUPPY IIA programs.

One of the main alterations was that the four-battery arrangement was dropped so as to provide more interior space, and a new battery ('Sargo II') was introduced. Provision was also made for a sonar room instead of having to use the deck gun magazine space as had been the case before conversion.

One *Tench* and nine *Balao*-Class boats were converted under the IA program, as shown in the accompanying table.

The GUPPY IA Program

PN	Name	Original Class	In Service	Shipyard	Conversion Complete
319	*Becuna*	Balao	44	EB	51
322	*Blackfin*	Balao	44	MI	51
323	*Caiman*	Balao	44	MI	51
324	*Blenny*	Balao	44	SF	51
341	*Chivo*	Balao	45	EB	51
342	*Chopper*	Balao	45	EB	51
403	*Atule*	Balao	44	Pts	51
406	*Sea Poacher*	Balao	44	Chas	52
407	*Sea Robin*	Balao	44	Pts	51
417	*Tench*	Tench	44	Pts	51

During the program SS-322, SS-403 and SS-417 were taken out of service and transferred to the reserve. The other boats remained in service during conversion.

147

Pennant numbers SS	Ships in the class		displacement surfaced submerged	Dimensions m			Output HP	Speed kn	Range Sm/kn	Oil fuel ts	Complement Officers/ enlisted	Original combat systems
	planned	completed		length	beam	draught						
319 322 – 324 341, 342 403, 406 407, 417	10 aus FY 51	10	1800 2400 bis 1870 2440	93,8	8,3		4610	17–18 15			~ 10/70	6 bow, 4 stern Torpedo tubes 21in

Powerplant: diesel-electric direct;
gearing and one auxiliary generator
diesel removed from some boats;
Sargo II batteries.

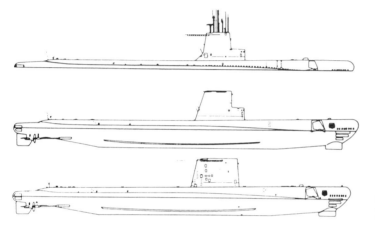

GUPPY IA conversion with Portsmouth conning tower.

GUPPY IA conversion with Electric Boat conning tower.

GUPPY IA and IIA conversion with plastics sail.

Undated photograph of *Becuna* (SS-319) with large sonar dome. [USN]

Blackfin (SS-322) in 1961. A Mare Island GUPPY IA conversion with Electric Boat-type conning tower. [USN]

An earlier photograph (1950s) of *Blackfin* wearing Measure SS 17G camouflage. [USN]

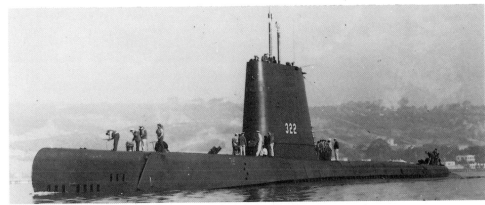

Blackfin again, now with plastics sail. [USN]

Blenny (SS-324), in the mid-1950s. [USN]

A later photograph of *Blenny* at Valletta, now (3 December 1966) with three BQG-4 antennae. [Pa]

Blenny was rebuilt at San Francisco, but had an Electric Boat conning tower, seen here at close quarters, with a PUFF antenna in the background, 1960. [USN]

Despite many reports that she had been used as a target boat, *Blenny* could still be seen at the Norfolk NISMF in 1988, fifteen years after having been stricken from the Navy Register. She is identifiable in this July 1983 photograph by her pennant number, still showing faintly through the obliterating paint. [WD]

Sea Poacher (SS-406), with crew at attention for the British Naval Review at Spithead, near Portsmouth, UK in June 1969 . A British submarine lies in the background. [Te]

Tench (SS-417), in the early 1970s. [USN] ▼

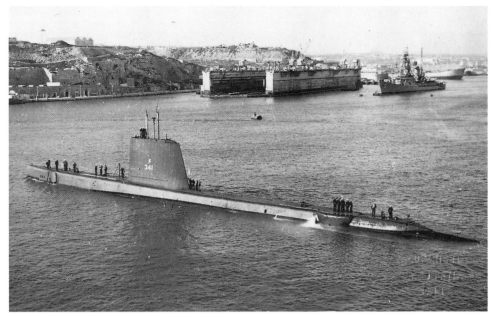

Chivo (SS-341), in Grand Harbour, Valletta, 14 March 1965; note the unusual bulge near the stern. [Pa]

Detail of the Portsmouth conning tower on Tench, Genoa, November 1961. [AB] ▼

Another photograph taken at Valletta, this time of Chopper (SS-342) on 24 March 1965. The British aircraft-carrier Centaur is in the background. [Pa]

In this aerial photograph of Hawkbill (SS-366), taken off Groton, Connecticut on 27 March 1953, the elegant hull form and the rounded edges of the deck are very clearly seen. [USN] ▶

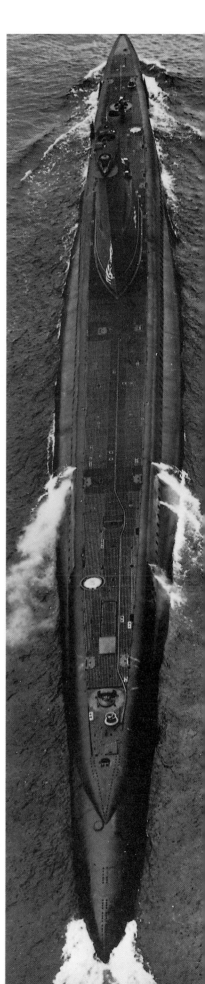

GUPPY IIA Conversions

The details of the GUPPY IIA conversion are linked with those of the IA models. There were problems with interior space in the IA conversion, and this led to the removal of one of the diesels and re-arrangement of the interior to provide a sonar control room in the GUPPY IIA boats. The loss of one engine, together with the reduction in battery power, resulted in somewhat lower speed and manoeuvrability, but this was compensated by better accommodation and easier maintenance.

The boats marked with an asterisk were withdrawn from the Reserve, and SS-340 and SS-365 had been 'in commission, in reserve', before their GUPPY IIA conversion. SS-366 and SS-367, originally intended for the GUPPY IIA program, were eventually transferred to GUPPY IB, while SS-394 and SS-418 were further modified for use as targets with the new generation of ASW torpedoes – minus warheads, of course!

PN	Name	Original Class	In Service	Shipyard	Conversion Complete
340	*Entemedor*	Balao	45	EB	52
365	*Hardhead*	Balao	44	EB	53
368	*Jallao**	Balao	44	MI	54
377	*Menhaden**	Balao	45	MI	53
382	*Picuda**	Balao	43	Pts	53
385	*Bang**	Balao	43	Pts	52
391	*Pomfret*	Balao	44	MI	53
394	*Razorback*	Balao	44	Pts	54
396	*Ronquil**	Balao	44	MI	53
402	*Sea Fox*	Balao	44	MI	53
410	*Threadfin*	Balao	44	Pts	53
415	*Stickleback*	Balao	45	MI	53
418	*Thornback*	Tench	44	Chas	53
420	*Tirante**	Tench	44	Pts	53
421	*Trutta**	Tench	44	Chas	53
424	*Quillback*	Tench	44	Pts	53

This 1954 photograph has a certain rarity value. It shows *Barb* (SS-220) on trials just after her GUPPY IB conversion but before her transfer to Italy. For the short period of her trials she was recommissioned into the US Navy. [AB]

Entemedor (SS-340) in 1962; a GUPPY IIA conversion with an Electric Boat-type conning tower. [MB]

Hardhead (SS-365) in May 1964. [USN]

152

Pennant numbers SS	Ships in the class		displacement surfaced submerged	Dimensions m			Output HP	Speed kn	Range Sm/kn	Oil fuel ts	Complement Officers/ enlisted	Original combat systems
	planned	completed		length	beam	draught						
340, 365 368, 377, 382, 385 391, 394 396, 402 410, 415 418, 420 421, 424	16 aus FY 52	16	1840 2445	93,3	8,3		3430	17–18 14–15			~ 10/75	6 bow, 4 stern Torpedo Tubes 21in

Powerplant: diesel-electric direct;
gearing and one auxiliary generator
diesel removed from some boats.
Sargo II batteries.

Jallao (SS-368), one of the Mare Island GUPPY IIAs, seen leaving the yard immediately after conversion, 23 January 1954. [USN]

Hardhead (SS-365), with sonar dome extended, receiving mail from the tender *Fulton* (AS-11), 27 August 1953. [USN]   ▼

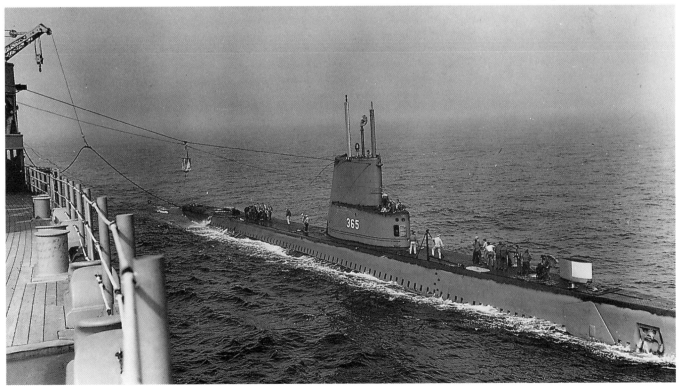

Hardhead (SS-365) in 1966. [USN]

A later photograph of *Jallao* with 'cap-feather' radio antenna on the plastics sail. The hydrophone has probably been lowered. [USN]

Menhaden (SS-377) seen in July 1957 after a spell at the San Francisco Naval Shipyard. [USN]

Bang (SS-385). [USN] ▲

Bang off the French Mediterranean coast, 8 February 1965. [MB]

Pomfret (SS-391) with a Portsmouth-type conning tower, 27 January 1953, immediately after her GUPPY IIA conversion at Mare Island. [USN]

Razorback (SS-394). [AB] ▶

155

STUB ANT.
COMM. INTERCEPT SYS.

PERISCOPE NO. 1
TYPE 8B

NT-66053
FIXED WHIP ANT.

PERISCOPE
NO. 2

"SS"
RADAR ANT.

NT-66053
RETRACTABLE WHIP ANT.

AS-468/B RADIO UHF ANT.

AT-317/BRR
VLF LOOP ANT.

Navy photograph of *Ronquil*'s (SS-396) conning-tower gear, 18 March 1960. [USN]

Ronquil's, elegant lines are seen in this early 1970s photograph, just before her transfer to Spain. Note the bulge in the after port quarter. [USN]

Sea Fox (SS-402), circa 1966. [AB]

Threadfin (SS-410), off the French Mediterranean coast, 16 May 1972. [MB]

Thornback (SS-418), off the French Riviera, 5 February 1964. [MB]

Tirante (SS-420); the deck hydrophone has a protective casing. [USN]

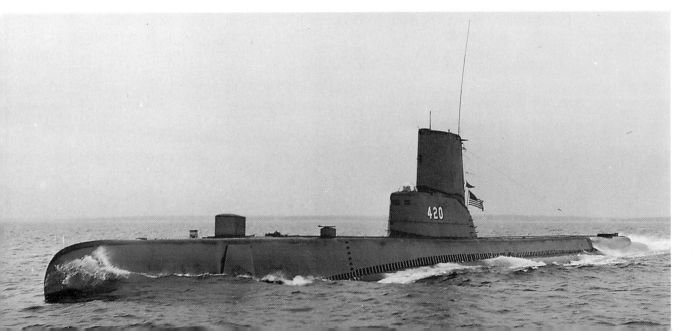

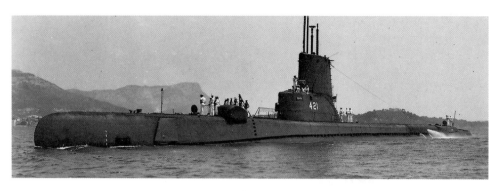

Trutta (SS-421) on 1 August 1964, off the French Mediterranean coast, with two access hatches open. [MB]

Quillback (SS-424) seen from the submarine tender *Bushnell* (AS-15), 27 July 1962. The 'cap-feather' antenna is extended, and there is a plexiglass weather screen to protect bridge personnel. [USN]

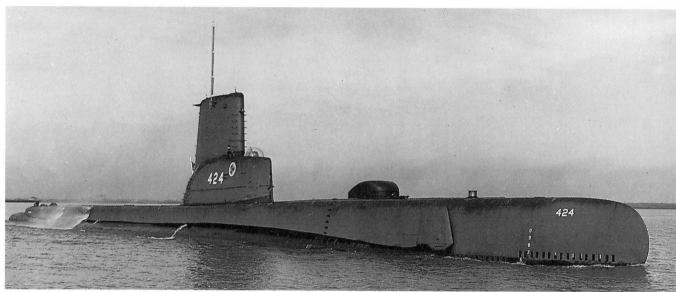

GUPPY IB Conversions

This was a rather special sub-section of the GUPPY series, in that only four boats were converted, of which two were transferred to Italy and two to the Netherlands. Before conversion, SS-220 and SS-247 had been taken out of service, while SS-366 and SS-367 were in the Reserve Fleet. All four were briefly recommissioned for trials and transfer. The GUPPY IB conversion was a slightly cheaper version of IA, but all four boats could be recognized by the GUPPY-type conning tower.

PN	Name	Original-Class	In Service	Shipyard	Conversion Complete
220	*Barb*	Gato	42	Pts	54
247	*Dace*	Gato	43	Pts	55
366	*Hawkbill*	Balao	44	EB	53
367	*Icefish*	Balao	44	EB	53

GUPPY III Conversions (FRAM II)

The Fleet Rehabilitation and Modernization Program (FRAM), which ran from 1958 to 1964,* extended by many years the service lives of hundreds of US warships. In essence, it consisted of integrating current battle systems into older hulls.

Some submarines were modernized within this framework. It had originally been intended to include 24 boats in the FRAM program, but this was reduced to nine on financial grounds. Apart from two boats of the *Sailfish* Class, these nine were GUPPY II fleet submarines. The finance for this operation was raised in Fiscal Year 1962.

One of the objects was to bridge the gap between the rapidly ageing fleet submarines and the coming nuclear boats. Current battle systems were installed and interior space was redistributed to provide better

* See, e.g., the Author's book *Das FRAM-Modernisierungsprogramm der US Navy*, Wehrwissenschaftliche Berichte Band 17, J. F. Lehmanns Verlag, Munich, 1975.

accommodation for a larger crew as well as to incorporate more electronics. To achieve this without reducing torpedo reload capability, a 4.6-metre section was inserted in the hull, principally to provide a new sonar room, although it also proved possible to extend the combat information centre (CIC) by 1.5 metres. All auxiliary machinery was either overhauled or replaced.

All nine boats had higher, mainly fibreglass, sails, although this was not exclusive to GUPPY III models, because quite a lot of other GUPPY boats both before and afterwards were fitted with this type of sail. However, the unmistakable sign of a GUPPY III was the three shark-fin PUFF antennae of the BQG-4 fire-control system. Of the previous GUPPY units, only *Blenny* (SS-324) had these antennae and, because she was also fitted with a plastics sail, the only distinguishing feature (especially when, as is often the case, the pennant number could not be seen) was that she was shorter.

The one exception within the GUPPY III type was *Tiru* (SS-416), in that she had only three main engines,

and the length of her inserted hull section was 3.8 metres instead of 4.6 metres. She was the last of the GUPPY IIIs, and left the Fleet in 1975. Because of the improvements made under the FRAM program, the GUPPY III boats were in considerable demand for transfer to other navies. In fact, seven boats were transferred, the remaining two being stricken after decommissioning.

PN	Name	Original-Class	In Service	Shipyard	Completed	GUPPY III Conversion	Conversion
343	Clamagore	Balao	45	EB	48	Chas	62
344	Cobbler	Balao	45	EB	49	Phil	62
346	Corporal	Balao	45	EB	48	Chas	62
351	Greenfish	Balao	46	Pts	48	Pearl	61
416	Tiru	Balao	–	MI	48	Pearl	59
425	Trumpetfish	Balao	46	Pts	48	Chas	62
487	Remora	Tench	45	MI	47	Pearl	62
490	Volador	Tench	–	Pts	48	SF	63
524	Pickerel	Tench	–	Pts	49	Pearl	62

GUPPY III (FRAM II) conversion with plastics sail and BQG-4 (PUFF) antennae.

Pennant numbers SS	Ships in the class		displacement surfaced submerged	Dimensions m			Output HP	Speed kn	Range Sm/kn	Oil fuel ts	Complement Officers/ enlisted	Original combat systems
	planned	completed		length	beam	draught						
343, 344 346, 351 416, 425 487, 490 542	24 aus FY 62	9	1975 2870	98,2 416: 97,3	8,3		3430	17 14			~ 10/85	6 bow, 4 stern torpedo tubes 53,3 cm (28 Torpedos)

Powerplant: see GUPPY II; SS-416 retained only 3 main generator diesels.

There are virtually no noticeable differences between the nine GUPPY III submarines. This February 1963 photograph shows *Clamagore* (SS-343) already fitted with the BQG-4 radar antenna. [WHD]

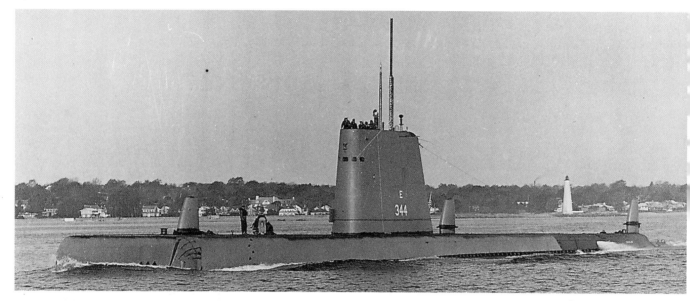

▲
Cobbler (SS-344). [USN]

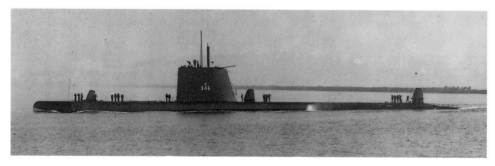

Corporal (SS-346) off Toulon, 2 February 1967. [MB]

Volador (SS-490) in January 1960, off Point Loma at the entrance to San Diego Bay. [USN]

In 1962 *Trumpetfish* (SS-425), seen here without her BQG-4 antennae, attended the Kiel Week Naval Review. She is seen here in the Kiel Canal near Holtenau on 6 June. [Te]

A photograph taken at the same time shows the high plastics sail of *Trumpetfish*. Judging by the crew's rig, the weather was very cool! The SUBRON 4 squadron emblem can be seen between the pennant number and the name plate. [Te]

Pickerel (SS-524) in 1962. [USN]

The Fleet Snorkel Program

In terms of what was actually done, this was not so much a conversion as a modification program. As we have already noted, even the less expensive aspects of the GUPPY program proved to be too costly, and so it proved impossible to convert more than a small preportion of the available fleet submarines. The fleet snorkel program was therefore established in Fiscal Year 1951, and was aimed at providing a minimal conversion consisting essentially of the addition of a snorkel. The actual fleet snorkel program extended over 1951-4 and included a total of eighteen boats. It should be noted here that the first snorkel had been fitted in *Irex* (SS-482) in 1947, long before the fleet snorkel program began. *Irex* also had what was for the time a new and unique form of conning tower, later replaced by a plastics sail.

The eighteen fleet snorkel program boats were also given GUPPY-type conning towers, of Electric Boat or Portsmouth design, although, again, during the last phase of their active service many boats were fitted with the higher, plastics sails. But in contrast to the GUPPY boats, the fleet snorkel hulls were not stream-lined, but retained the original form which favoured surface rather than submerged operation. This of course makes them immediately recognizable: GUPPY boats all have rounded bows, whereas fleet snorkels and other unmodified boats have the original raked stem.

All the fleet snorkel modifications were carried out during normal refits. In a few cases, after the modific-ations had been effected, deck and conning tower guns were retained to improve stability. Where arma-ment was removed, additional sonar equipment was installed.

During modification, all vessels remained in com-mission; SS-348 had previously been SSG, and SS-399, AGSS. The fleet snorkel program was not financed out of SCN funds, but out of the mainten-ance and overhaul program. Unlike the GUPPYs, the fleet snorkels were taken out of service at the beginning of the 1970s.

Fleet Snorkel Conversions

PN	Name	Original Class	In service	Con-version	Con-verted
302	*Sabalo*	Balao	45	Pearl	52
303	*Sablefish*	Balao	45	Phil	51
320	*Bergall*	Balao	44	Phil	52
328	*Charr*	Balao	44	MI	51
331	*Bugara*	Balao	44	Pearl	51
337	*Carbonero*	Balao	45	MI	52
338	*Carp*	Balao	45	SF	52
348	*Cusk*	Balao	45	MI	54
392	*Sterlet*	Balao	44	SF	52
398	*Segundo*	Balao	44	SF	51
399	*Sea Cat*	Balao	44	Phil	52
405	*Sea Owl*	Balao	44	Phil	51
408	*Sennet*	Balao	44	Phil	52
409	*Piper*	Balao	44	Chas	51
423	*Torsk*	Tench	44	Pts	52
475	*Argonaut*	Tench	45	Phil	52
476	*Runner*	Tench	45	Chas	52
480	*Medregal*	Tench	45	Chas	52
482	*Irex*	Tench	45	Pts	47

Sabalo (SS-302) was one of two fleet snorkels rebuilt at Pearl Harbor Naval Shipyard, where the new GUPPY-type conning tower and snorkel were installed. This photo-graph was taken off Hawaii on 29 September 1953.

Pennant numbers	Ships in the class		displacement surfaced	Dimensions m			Output HP	Speed kn	Range Sm/kn	Oil fuel ts	Comple- ment	Original combat systems
SS	plan- ned	com- pleted	submerged	length	beam	draught					Officers/ enlisted	
302, 303 320, 328 331, 337 338, 348 392, 398 399, 405 408, 409 423, 475 476, 480 482	19 aus FY 51 bis FY 54	19	2040 2410	95,2	8,3		4610	18 9			~ 10/73	1 - 5in L/25, 1 - 40 mm (later removed) 6 Bow, 4 Stern torpedo tube (21-28 Torpedoes)

Powerplant: direct diesel-electric;
gearing and one auxiliary generator
diesel removed from some boats.

Fleet snorkel type with Portsmouth conning tower.

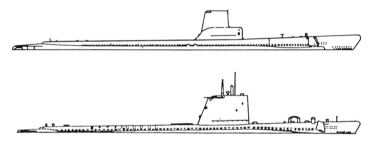

Irex in 1964, fleet snorkel type with plastics sail.

Ten years after the fleet snorkel modification: *Sablefish* (SS-303) with plastics sail and sonar dome, 18 May 1961. [USN]

Sablefish more than three years later, off the French Mediterranean coast on 13 November 1964. [MB]

Bugara (SS-331) in San Francisco Bay, 13 March 1958. Both photographs show clearly the sharply angled decks and stem, which were the most notable difference between the fleet snorkels and the GUPPYs. The small antennae indicate SS-2 radar. [USN]

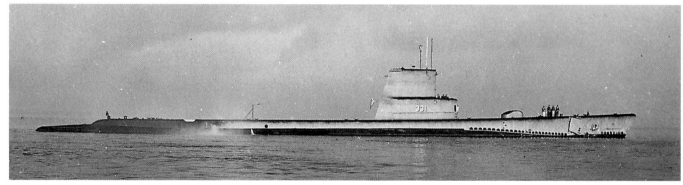

Carp (SS-338), 10 September 1962. [MB]

Sea Cat (SS-399), September 1963. [USN]

Sea Cat (SS-399) in Grand Harbour, Valletta, on 12 April 1961. [Pa]

Sea Owl (SS-405) berthing at Genoa in September 1965. [GGh]

Another photograph of *Sea Owl* (SS-405) showing her most notable feature, the prominent sonar dome for the BQR-4 sonar. Similar sonar domes were fitted in *Sterlet* (SS-392) and *Piper* (SS-409). [USN] ▼

Sea Owl at Toulon in 1966, giving a view of the BQR-4 sonar dome. [MB]

Piper (SS-409) was also fitted with BQR-4 sonar. [USN]

Torsk (SS-423) in Hampton Roads, Norfolk, Virginia, on 5 May 1959. [USN]

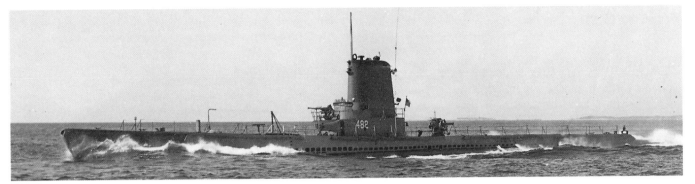

Of all the fleet snorkel group, *Irex* carried the highest pennant number (SS-482), although she was by definition the first fleet snorkel converted before the extensive 1951 program began. This 1951 photograph shows *Irex* after the snorkel and the uniquely shaped conning tower had been installed. She still has 5in and 40mm deck armament. [USN]

Six years later: *Irex* off Toulon, 21 November 1957. Her conning tower has lost its forward cigarette deck along with the 40mm AA armament, although the 5in L/25 deck gun is still in place. [MB] ▶

More than 10 years later (29 February 1968): *Irex*, again off Toulon, now has a plastics sail and no deck armament. [MB]

Undated photograph of *Irex*. Her sonar dome is clearly visible in the location formerly occupied by the JP hydrophones. [USN] ▼

Radar Submarines

First Attempts

The first radar picket submarines were produced in response to Japanese *kamikaze* attacks. It was realized that outlying submarines could spot enemy aircraft earlier than surface-vessel escorts. They could dive for their own protection once they had spotted incoming enemy aircraft, thus avoiding the heavy losses that had been inflicted upon radar picket destroyers [DDR].

Without being reclassified as SSR, therefore, slight modifications were carried out on SS-481 and SS-489. They retained their deck armament, but had additional radar antennae from the surface-vessel inventory fitted to their after decks. Because of the haste with which these alterations were carried out, there were problems with positional accuracy of the sternmost radar arrays. Without actually changing course, therefore, the Navy instituted the 'Migraine' program, which developed in three successively improving phases.

Migraine I

In this first design improvement, SS-419 and (later) SS-312 underwent quite significant modification both internally and externally. The crew accommodation and the galley, located beneath the after part of the conning tower, were converted to an air-control centre, and new space for crew and equipment was provided by removing two of the bow and all of the stern tubes. Radar antennae of Types SS, SV-1, SV-2, and BPS-2 were fitted, well separated from one another and mounted on pillars. Homing beacon equipment was the YE-2 antenna, a forerunner of TACAN. One gun was removed, and a snorkel was fitted.

Migraine II

This design consisted essentially of further modification of the first two radar picket submarines, SS-481 and SS-489, which were then reclassified as SSR. In this design, the air-control centre was astern, in place of the torpedo tubes. The battery rooms remained unchanged, but were fitted with the new, higher-capacity Sargo-II batteries. Both deck guns were removed and a snorkel installed. A notable feature was the SV-2 heightfinder antenna installed low on the after deck, which clearly distinguishes this type from Migraine I. Under the Migraine II design, SS, SV, SV-2, and SR-2 radars were fitted, as well as the YE-3 homing beacon for aircraft approach.

Migraine III

The concentration of so much electronic equipment in such limited space caused special problems. Despite the considerable surface-vessel experience gained during the War, effective placement of radar equipment in the relatively small hull of a submarine was something yet to be mastered. Six *Gato*-Class boats were therefore allocated for conversion according to the Migraine III design from 1951 to 1953. In order to provide space for an air-control centre, a 7.3-metre hull section was inserted between the forward battery room and the combat information centre. Nevertheless, it was still necessary to remove the after torpedo tubes to provide accommodation for additional crew. These boats were also fitted with snorkels and newer, higher, enclosed conning towers. All these conversions were finished by 1953, and to complete their renewal the boats were fitted with up-to-date BPS-2, BPS-3 and BPS-4 radars.

The entire radar-picket concept, including the radar submarines, came to an end in the late 1950s, when the Navy abandoned the idea in favour of early-warning aircraft. This applied also to the two *Sailfish*-Class SSRs and even to the nuclear *Triton* (SSRN-586), which were reclassified SS and SSN respectively. Similarly, the previously converted SSRs were reclassified SS or AGSS and remained so until their final decommissioning about a decade later.

Various Radar Picket Conversions

PN	Name	Original-Class	Migraine	In Service	Ship yard	Conversion Complete
481	*Requin*	Tench	II	45	Pts	46/48
489	*Spinax*	Tench	II	–	Pts	46/48
419	*Tigrone*	Tench	I	44	Pts	49
312	*Burrfish*	Balao	I	43	Pts	50
267	*Pompon*	Gato	III	43	Phil	53
269	*Rasher*	Gato	III	43	Phil	53
270	*Raton*	Gato	III	43	Phil	53
271	*Ray*	Gato	III	43	Phil	53
272	*Redfin*	Gato	III	43	Phil	53
274	*Rock*	Gato	III	43	Phil	53

Migraine I SSR Conversions

| Pennant numbers SSR | Ships in the class | | displacement surfaced submerged | Dimensions m | | | Output HP | Speed kn | Range Sm/kn | Oil fuel ts | Comple-ment Officers/ enlisted | Original combat systems |
	plan-ned	com-pleted		length	beam	draught						
312, 419	2 aus FY 48/49	2	312: 2085 2410 419: 2005 2410	95,2	8,3		4610				~ 12/90	1 - 40 mm (later removed) 4 bow-TR
												Radar: SS, SV-1, SV-2, BPS-2; Fighter Control YE-2

Powerplant: direct diesel-electric;
gearing removed from SS-312; two
126-cell batteries.

Migraine II SSR Conversions

| Pennant numbers SSR | Ships in the class | | displacement surfaced submerged | Dimensions m | | | Output HP | Speed kn | Range Sm/kn | Oil fuel ts | Comple-ment Officers/ enlisted | Original combat systems |
	plan-ned	com-pleted		length	beam	draught						
481, 489	2 aus FY 48	2	1985 2410	95,2	8,3		4610	18 9			~ 10/85	1 - 40 mm (later removed) 4 bow-TR
												Radar: SS, SV-1 SV-2, SR-2 Fighter Control YE-3

Powerplant: as *Tench*-Class, but
with Sargo batteries.

Migraine III SSR Conversions

| Pennant numbers SSR | Ships in the class | | displacement surfaced submerged | Dimensions m | | | Output HP | Speed kn | Range Sm/kn | Oil fuel ts | Comple-ment Officers/ enlisted | Original combat systems |
	plan-ned	com-pleted		length	beam	draught						
267 269 – 272 274	6 aus FY 51/53	6	2308	104,2	8,3		4610	17 8			~ 12/95	6 bow-TR 21in (10 long, 2 short Torpedoes)
												Radar: BPS-2, BPS-3, BPS-4

Powerplant: direct diesel-electric;
gearing removed. Original drive and
batteries; 2 main diesel motors.

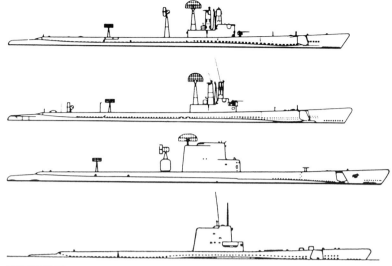

SSR Migraine I conversion, with deck gun.

SSR Migraine II conversion, without deck gun.

SSR Migraine III conversion.

Redfin (ex-SSR), in AGSS configuration.

Spinax (SS-489) in 1946-7. She was one of the first radar submarines, but without SSR classification. Two 40mm deck guns remain, and on the after deck just above the name is a Heightfinder SV-2 radar although no YE-2 beacon can be seen. *Spinax* was converted during her actual building whereas her sister boat *Requin* (SS-481) was converted after she had been delivered as a fleet submarine. [USN]

The first example of the Migraine I rebuild was *Tigrone* (SSR-419) seen here off Toulon, 26 October 1951. Only the 40mm anti-aircraft gun remains. There is an alarming mix of equipment packed around the conning tower On the right we can identify SS-2, the later SJ antenna; the large antenna is an SR-2 (now belonging to BPS-2 equipment), on the after deck is an SV-2 and, well aft, the YE-2 beacon. [MB]

Fifteen months later (21 February 1953), again off Toulon, *Tigrone* is seen without further alteration. [MB]

Burrfish (SSR-312), off the French Riviera in 1951. She received Migraine I modifications similar to *Tigrone*'s. [AB]

As part of the Migraine II modification, the performance of the first two radar submarines was upgraded. Here we see *Requin*, now with SSR-481 classification, in the Mediterranean on 27 March 1951. The SR-2 radar antenna is now mounted on the conning tower and in its former position is the YE-3 fighter homing beacon. There is still a single 40mm anti-aircraft gun forward, but this was removed in 1955. [MB]

Requin: detail of the conning tower with its clutter of equipment. The small radar antennae are SS-2 and SJ, and an SR-2 can be seen at the right. [AB]

171

In August 1959 *Requin* was again reclassified as SS-481 and her appearance was that of a normal fleet snorkel, 15 May 1967. [Pa]

Both these photographs of *Spinax* (SSR-489), taken on 23 May 1950, show clearly that she was modified along the lines of *Requin*. On this Mediterranean patrol she carried no pennant number. [MB]

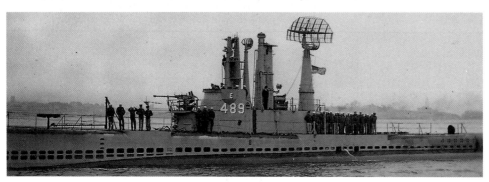

Another detailed photograph of *Spinax*. The low round structure aft of the SJ antenna is the air inlet head of the snorkel apparatus. [MB]

In mid-1959, *Spinax* was also reclassified SS-489 and returned to fleet snorkel status. At the same time she was fitted with a new, specially shaped conning tower. 8 May 1961. [USN]   ▼

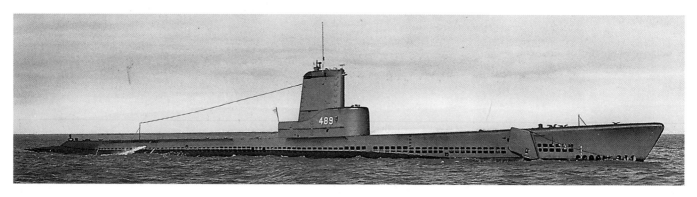

The lengthening of the hull and the installation of a new conning tower were the most important visible aspects of the Migraine III modification. This undated photograph shows *Pompon* (SSR-267) with the number and type of radar apparatus indicating a Migraine II configuration, except that the SR-2 is now designated BPS-2. No deck armament remains. [USN]

◄
Pompon at Valletta, Malta on 23 July 1951, with no YE-3 antenna visible. [Pa]

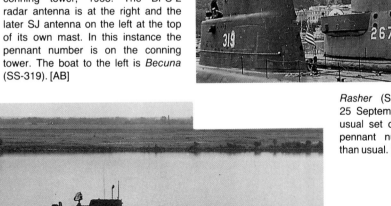

Detailed photograph of *Pompon*'s conning tower, 1958. The BPS-2 radar antenna is at the right and the later SJ antenna on the left at the top of its own mast. In this instance the pennant number is on the conning tower. The boat to the left is *Becuna* (SS-319). [AB]

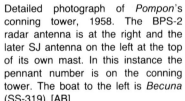

Rasher (SSR-269) off Philadelphia, 25 September 1953. She carries the usual set of radar antennae, but the pennant number is further forward than usual. [USN]

Raton (SSR-270) off San Francisco Naval Shipyard, 20 November 1958. The large antenna is for a BPS-2 radar. [USN] ▼

In mid-1970 *Raton* was reclassified AGSS, without ever having been 'SS'. This undated photograph was taken during this period in her service life. [USN]

Ray (SSR-271), 24 April 1954. [MB]

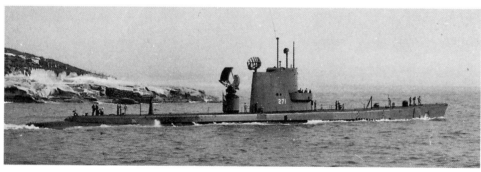

Ray about two years later (23 April 1956). In place of the heightfinder SV-2 a BPS-3 radar antenna has been installed. [Pa]

This photograph of the after deck of *Redfin* (SSR-272) taken on 17 June 1956 shows details of the YE-3 homing beacon antenna in the foreground and the BPS-3 behind it. [AN]

Rock (SSR-274) off Philadelphia Naval Shipyard, 3 December 1953, after her Migraine III conversion. It almost looks as though the censor has blanked out the SV-3 antenna. [USN]

In this undated photograph of *Rock* no SV-3 antenna is visible either. The pennant number can be seen forward on the conning tower's bulwark. [USN]

These two photographs show *Rock* on 21 August 1961. Reclassified in December 1959 to AGSS-274, all large radar antennae have been removed and the pennant number is now in the usual place. [USN]

At some time both deck-mounted antennae were removed from *Rock* so that here only the conning tower BPS-2 remains. This photograph was taken off Mare Island on 28 July 1958. [USN]

Guided Missile Submarines

Loon Conversions

At the end of the War, the Allies captured a number of German V-weapons, most notably the V-1 'flying bomb'. In considering their use as ship-launched weapons, it soon became apparent that fleet submarines might well make suitable launch platforms. In Fiscal Year 1948, therefore, the conversion of two *Balao*-Class boats, SS-348 and SS-337, was approved and funded. It is worth noting, however, that in January 1948 *Cusk* was given the new classification SSG (keeping the same pennant number), while *Carbonero* retained her 'SS' classification. Launch equipment was fitted to SS-348 and later to SS-337.

At first *Carbonero* acted only as a relay and support ship for the Loon missile, but later both units had cylindrical, watertight hangars for two of the missiles fitted aft of their conning towers. The circular doors of these hangars were designed to open sideways. Both boats had electronic control systems installed, but it is not widely known that similar equipment was fitted to other fleet submarines so that they could take over control of the missile once it had passed beyond the range of the launch vessel.

When the Loon experimental programme ended in 1953, *Cusk*, reclassified 'SS', was reconverted to a fleet snorkel (the snorkel itself was already fitted), but *Carbonero* remained as part of the first all-American Regulus missile program until 1961, when she became once again an active fleet submarine.

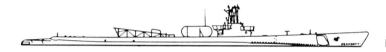

Loon-SSG, appearance.

Loon SSG Conversions

Pennant numbers	Ships in the class		displacement surfaced	Dimensions m			Output HP	Speed kn	Range Sm/kn	Oil fuel ts	Complement	Original combat systems
SSG SS	planned	completed	submerged	length	beam	draught					Officers/ enlisted	
348, 337	2	2	2075	95,2	8,3		4610	17			~ 10/74	6 bow, 4 stern torpedo tubes 21in, 2 Loon missiles
	aus FY 48		2400					8				

Powerplant: direct diesel-electric; gearing removed; drive motors as *Tench* class.

Carbonero (SS-337) before the launch of a Loon missile, 26 August 1949. She was later fitted with the same type of cylindrical missile hangar as *Cusk* [USN].

SSG Conversion of SS-282

In March 1953 *Tunny* (SS-282) was converted to take part in tests of the Regulus I missile, which later remained in service for quite some time in surface ships. In addition to a fleet snorkel conversion *Tunny* was fitted with a GUPPY conning tower, a retractable launch ramp and, in front of it, a large cylindrical hangar for two missiles, with an upwards-opening door. Missile control equipment was fitted in an internal control centre, which necessitated the removal of one main and one auxiliary diesel. This boat carried Regulus I missiles successfully until the end of the program and, in 1965, briefly reverted to fleet snorkel before further conversion to transport submarine at the end of 1966.

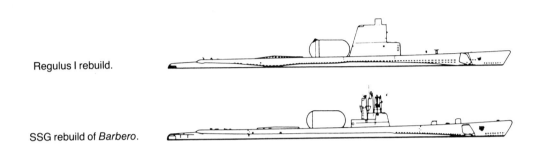

Regulus I rebuild.

SSG rebuild of *Barbero*.

Regulus I Conversion: SSG-282

Pennant numbers	Ships in the class		displacement surfaced	Dimensions m			Output HP	Speed kn	Range Sm/kn	Oil fuel ts	Complement	Original combat systems
SSG	planned	completed	submerged	length	beam	draught					Officers/ enlisted	
282	1	1	2075	95,2	8,3		3430	17			~ 10/74	6 bow, 4 stern torpedo tubes 21in, 2 Regulus I missiles
			2400				2740	9				

Powerplant: direct diesel-electric; gearing removed; as was one main and one auxiliary generator diesel.

Tunny (SSG-282) on 7 July 1953, two months after her second commissioning. [USN]

A Regulus I cruise missile being loaded aboard *Tunny*. [AB]

This detailed photograph of *Tunny* at Yokosuka, Japan, on 12 October 1962, shows her conning tower, and the missile hangar together with the deck extension needed to support it. [T.Kamiya]

Barbero (SSG-317), with crew lining the deck and a Regulus I on the launching ramp, June 1957. [LvG])

This 1958 photograph clearly shows the deck extension in the area of the hangar, and the effect of the roughly applied camouflage on *Barbero*. [USN]

SSG Conversion of SS-317

Up to 1955 *Barbero* was a cargo submarine classified ASSA-317. Her SSG conversion was an intermediate stage, the intention being that there should be another Regulus I submarine besides *Tunny* until delivery of the first new boats capable of carrying Regulus II. However, the Regulus II program was soon to be suspended in favour of Polaris (ICBM). During her earlier refit in 1948 *Barbero* had lost two main diesels and her stern tubes. Now, a missile control centre was installed forward of the after battery room. Steps to improve stability were also taken: a ballast channel was cut in the keel, into which 150 tons of lead was poured. The launching ramp and missile hangar were identical with those in *Tunny*, but the conning tower remained more or less in its original form despite the addition of more equipment and a snorkel. It is also worth noting that the hangar was set 'on the hump' to provide access to the boat's interior. In fact, six crew members shared sleeping quarters with the Regulus missile in the hangar. Three years after the end of the Regulus I program, the much-rebuilt and overworked *Barbero* was decommissioned and stricken from the Naval Vessels Register (NVR).

Various SSG Conversions

PN	Name	Original Class	In Service	Shipyard	Conversion Complete
348	*Cusk*	Balao	46	MI	48
337	*Carbonero*	Balao	45	–	49
282	*Tunny*	Gato	42	MI	53
317	*Barbero*	Balao	44	MI	56

Regulus I Conversion: SSG-317

Pennant numbers SSG	Ships in the class		displacement surfaced	Dimensions m			Output HP	Speed kn	Range Sm/kn	Oil fuel ts	Complement Officers/ enlisted	Original combat systems
	plan- ned	com- pleted	submerged	length	beam	draught						
317	1	1	2130	95,2	8,3		2305	14			~ 10/75	6 bow-TR 21in 2
	aus FY 55		2410				2740	9				Regulus I missiles

Powerplant: direct diesel-electric;
gearing had been removed earlier;
two main generator diesels removed.

Various Freight, Tanker and Transport Conversions

Freight Submarine Conversion

It may be recalled that, in 1943, the US Navy converted the three boats of the B Class (SS-163 to SS-165) to cargo submarines without reclassifying them. After that, the Navy had only one more cargo submarine, *Barbero* (SS-317), which was rebuilt and reclassified SSA in 1948, then reclassified yet again as ASSA at the beginning of 1950. Removal of the stern torpedo tubes released space for about 120 tons of cargo, plus space in the forward engine room and in part of the after battery room. Cargo was loaded through newly installed hatches which served both deck and cargo spaces. Further re-arrangement included relocating the crew accommodation to the forward battery room, and converting two of the fuel tanks to hold some 107 tons of gasoline. New engines and a snorkel were also fitted. After only a few years, however, the cargo submarine was no longer considered viable, and in 1956 *Barbero* was reconverted to ASSG as described above.

Transport Submarine Conversion: SSA-317

PN	Name	Original-Class	In Service	Shipyard	Conversion Complete
317	*Barbero*	Balao	44	MI	48

Troop Transport Submarine Conversions

The idea of using submarines as troop transports arose during the Second World War; it may be recalled that *Argonaut* (SS-166) was converted for that purpose in 1942. She was given the designation APS-1, but the APS designation was never used again. In general, it was these transport submarines that suffered the most changes in designation (while retaining their pennant numbers: see section on Classification).

It was certainly due to experience in the War that the idea of submarine troop transports took hold, and at the end of the War a large number of suitable submarines was available. Clearly submarine troop transports could be very useful for landing beach-master parties in advance of amphibious operations. It was not intended that the role of submarine transports should usurp or even supplement that of large surface transports. They were seen more as instruments by which assault commandos, frogmen, or amphibious sabotage units and their equipment could be landed rapidly and stealthily.

In 1948 SS-313 and SS-315 were converted and reclassified SSP, and were available by the end of that year with room for:

- a maximum of 111 troops
- 85 tons of weapons and equipment
- a complete chain-driven amphibious vehicle (LVT) and a jeep
- eight inflatables that could carry ten men each.

In order to achieve this, yet another conversion of the internal arrangement was necessary. The forward engine was removed, as were the torpedo tubes, to provide cargo and accommodation space. Deck armament was left alone at first, but was removed later. A notable addition was the large cylindrical hangar similar to those of the SSG conversions, but with a side-opening door. More access hatches were provided along the deck, one of which opened into the hangar where the jeep, the floats and the LVT were stowed. New main engines were fitted and, while the conning tower retained its original form, it bristled with periscopes, radar masts and snorkel tubes.

During their service lives, both boats underwent several further modifications. In particular, the hangars were removed. Before they had been installed, the deck had been widened to allow access past them, and now this bulge proved to be useful as a helicopter landing pad. After the hangars had been removed the rubber rafts were stored inboard and were not inflated until they were needed. A simple and practical method was devised for launching them. Once inflated, they were arranged forward and aft of the conning tower with troops and equipment in place, then the submarine submerged until her decks were awash, and they floated off, to be silently steered ashore. To have launched them over the side of the relatively high deck would have been much more

difficult, and loading them would have been extremely noisy.

Both boats were successively reclassified SSP, ASSP, APSS and LPSS over their relatively long service lives, and Perch was briefly a training hulk with the designation IXSS-313 before she finished her time. Because of her special capabilities, Perch had in fact seen service in amphibious landings in both Korea and Vietnam. Sealion, last of the old fleet submarines, served in the Atlantic and was transferred to the reserve in 1970, before being stricken in 1977.

Turning back now to Tunny, which was SSG-282 when we last referred to her, we find that she was briefly reclassified 'SS' at the end of that phase of her service and then, very late in her life, was reclassified again to APSS in 1966. This was an obvious consequence of the modifications made during her SSG conversion. At the beginning of 1969 she was LPSS for a few months before being finally stricken. The general characteristics of Tunny were similar to those of the other two boats.

Transport Submarine Conversion

PN	Name	Original-Class	In Service	Shipyard	Conversion Complete
313	Perch	Balao	44	MI	48
315	Sealion	Balao	44	SF	48
282	Tunny	Gato	42	Pug	66

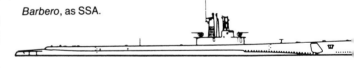

Barbero, as SSA.

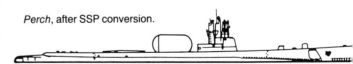

Perch, after SSP conversion.

Cargo Submarine Conversion: SSA-317

Pennant numbers SSA	Ships in the class		displacement surfaced submerged	Dimensions m			Output HP	Speed kn	Range Sm/kn	Oil fuel ts	Comple- ment Officers/ enlisted	Original combat systems
	plan- ned	com- pleted		length	beam	draught						
317	1	1	2130	95,2	8,3		2305	14			~ 6/55	6 bow-TR 21in
	aus FY 48		2410					9				

Powerplant: Direct diesel-electric;
gearing plus 2 main generator
diesels and 2 main diesels removed.

Transport Submarine Conversions: SSP-313 Class

Pennant numbers SSP	Ships in the class		displacement surfaced submerged	Dimensions m			Output HP	Speed kn	Range Sm/kn	Oil fuel ts	Comple- ment Officers/ enlisted	Original combat systems
	plan- ned	com- pleted		length	beam	draught						
313, 315	2	2	2160	95,2	8,3		2305	14			~ 6/68	1 - 5in L/25, 1 - 40 mm (both removed later. No Torpedo tubes
	aus FY 48		2410				2740	8				

Powerplant: Direct diesel-electric;
gearing and 2 main generator
diesels removed.

Perch as APSS after removal of hangar.

Transport Submarine Conversion: APSS-282

Pennant numbers APSS	Ships in the class		displacement surfaced submerged	Dimensions m			Output HP	Speed kn	Range Sm/kn	Oil fuel ts	Comple- ment Officers/ enlisted	Original combat systems
	plan- ned	com- pleted		length	beam	draught						
282	1	1	2075	95,2	8,3		3430	17			~ 6/68	No data on torpedo tubes
	aus FY 66		2400				2740	9				

Powerplant: see SSG-282

Midships detail of *Perch* seen here as ASSP-313 in 1955. [AB]

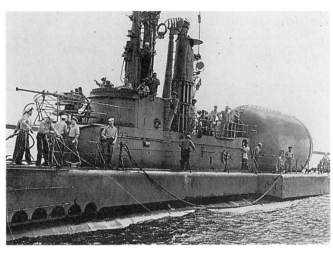

Perch after reclassification as APSS-313, seen here on 4 December 1961: the hangar has been removed but the deck extension remains. A helicopter can land here in emergencies.

Sealion, seen here (28 April 1953) as ASSP-315 but without hangar. The 5in L/25 deck gun and the forward 40mm anti-aircraft gun are still visible. The amount of gear on the conning tower was a cause of considerable underwater turbulence and had an adverse effect on speed, which led to the introduction of the hydrodynamic GUPPY-type tower. [USN]

◀ This 1956 photograph shows a joint exercise with Marines aboard *Sealion*, now in her APSS classification, using inflatables and a helicopter. [USN]

In January 1969 *Sealion* was once again reclassified, this time as LPSS, and this photograph (*circa* 1969-71) was taken after that reclassification. She is now painted black, and carries two 40mm anti-aircraft guns. [USN]   ▼

Tanker Submarine Conversions

PN	Name	Original Class	In Service	Shipyard	Conversion Complete
362	*Guavina*	Gato	43	MI	50
362	*Guavina*	Gato	–	Chas	57

Using funds from Fiscal Year 1949, SS-362 was reconverted as a submarine tanker and reclassified SSO (submarine oiler) from the middle of 1948. The object was to use the boat in amphibious operations, and the most important modification was the addition outside the pressure hull of side-blister tanks with a capacity of 362 tons of fuel oil. These, plus the tanks already in place, gave the vessel a total fuel-carrying capacity of 605 tons, and the external tanks were not visible in normal trim, although beam had been increased by about 3 metres. A snorkel and new engines were installed, and all but two of the after torpedo tubes were removed to provide more cargo and accommodation space.

In amphibious operations, *Guavina* was intended to supply fuel for landing parties, but, some years later, this idea was dropped, and she was reclassified AGSS at the end of 1951. The second phase of her service life began in 1957, with the development of the jet-powered Seamaster P6M flying-boat. In order to be able to refuel this aircraft at sea, *Guavina* was returned to tanker service, and reclassified yet again, this time as AOSS.

The main modifications carried out were the addition of a streamlined GUPPY-type sail and a ramp over the stern from which the flying-boat could be refuelled. However, the P6M program was discontinued, although photographic records do show that *Guavina* was used to refuel the earlier P5M Marlin flying-boat. With the ending of the P6M program, the submarine tanker became redundant and *Guavina* ended her days as a training hulk before being finally stricken in 1967.

Submarine Tanker Conversion SSO-362

Pennant numbers	Ships in the class		displacement surfaced	Dimensions m			Output HP	Speed kn	Range Sm/kn	Oil fuel ts	Comple-ment	Original combat systems
SSO	planned	completed	submerged	length	beam	draught					Officers/ enlisted	
362	1	1	2733	95,0	11,7			16		605	~ 8/68	2 stern-TR 21 in (6 Torpedoes)
	aus FY 49, als AOSS aus FY 57		2950				2740	7				

Powerplant: direct diesel-electric;
gearing removed; 2 main diesels.

Guavina is seen here as SSO-362, which dates the photograph to between 1948 and the end of 1951. [AB]

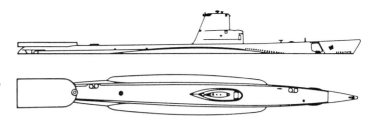

AOSS *Guavina* after conversion, 1957.

Guavina, seen off Norfolk, Virginia, on 5 March 1955, while she was classified AGSS-362. A P5M flying-boat, requesting refuelling, approaches the stern ramp of the submarine. Also in the picture is the salvage ship *Escape* (ARS-6). [USN]

Auxiliary Submarine Reclassification (AGSS)

The AGSS category was used for vessels that were no longer in the first line of fleet submarines, but were assigned to any one of a number of special tasks. In fact, many of them were used for research and development – see, e.g., the descriptions of *Dolphin* (AGSS-555) and *Albacore* (AGSS-569). Within this category, there were two main groups:

■ seven units extensively rebuilt to carry out specified functions;
■ a total of 74 other fleet boats which, for administrative purposes, were nominally reclassified AGSS from 1959 to 1961 without rebuilding; many an old friend from other categories can be found in this group!

Various AGSS-Conversions

PN	Name	Original Class	In Service	Shipyard	Conversion Complete
299	*Manta*	Balao	44	SF	49
318	*Baya**	Balao	44	MI u.a.	49
399	*Sea Cat**	Balao	44	Phil.	50
229	*Flying Fish**	Gato	41	Pts (?)	50
214	*Grouper**	Gato	42	Pts	60
311	*Archerfish*	Balao	43	Phil	60
419	*Tigrone**	Tench	44	Phil	64

Before going into detail, it should be noted that, of the seven boats listed above, five (indicated by an asterisk) were used for acoustic or other research purposes. The descriptions of the various conversions below follow in chronological order of completion.

In Fiscal Year 1949 *Manta* (AGSS-299) was modified to serve as an underwater target. The new generation of homing torpedoes had to be tested under realistic conditions, but without warheads so as to avoid damage to the target boat. These pre-programmed, extremely aggressive weapons located their objective by means of their homing head, selected a target, then turned and aimed themselves to strike its hull amidships. Since the training version did not explode and could not be switched off, it kept to its task and continued to ram the hull until it ran out of fuel. As *Manta* was single-hulled, external blisters were fitted along the length of the hull to absorb these hits. The forward and after torpedo rooms were filled with balsa wood, the tubes were sealed off, and the forward engine room was converted to crew accommodation. These measures worked – *Manta* was never sunk by one of these torpedoes.

Again in 1949, in response to a design request from the Naval Electronics Laboratory, *Baya* (AGSS-318) underwent the first of a series of conversions that was to continue until her end in 1972. Up to 1959 she showed very little external evidence of these alterations, as they consisted mainly of the installation of one item of electronic equipment after another. The first visible alteration came in mid-1959, with the addition of a bulbous bow extension to house the LORAD (Long-Range Active Radar Detection) equipment. Later, in 1968, *Baya* was to be seen with three early versions of the PUFF antenna. In general, the details of *Baya*'s conversions were withheld on security grounds, but it is known that in 1959 a 7-metre section was inserted in her hull to house the LORAD test equipment. It is also known that all torpedo tubes were sealed off, then removed entirely, to provide space for laboratory and electronic equipment, as well as accommodation for civilian scientific and technical personnel.

There followed in 1950 a relatively moderate rebuild of *Flying Fish* (SS-229) and *Sea Cat* (SS-399) for testing sonar equipment, such as, for example, the XDG search sonar that was installed in *Sea Cat*. Alterations to *Flying Fish* were clearly visible: on the otherwise unchanged conning tower, hydrophones of the passive sonar equipment from the German cruiser *Prinz Eugen* were installed, protected by a drum projecting over the edge of the deck. The results of this research led to the introduction of more efficient passive sonars in American submarines. Because the modifications had been so slight, it was possible to return both submarines to their original configurations after the completion of the test programme.

As will be seen in the following section, *Grouper* was the first US submarine to be rebuilt as a hunter-killer (SSK) after the end of the Second World War. Eighteen months after reclassification as AGSS, her reconstruction as a sonar research vessel was completed – or at least the first phase of a series of modifications that would continue until 1968. The design for the sonar research-vessel configuration was carried out by the Naval Underwater Laboratory, an organization which *Grouper* served until 1968. During the rebuilding, the after torpedo tubes were taken out of service, and the forward tubes removed entirely to house the sonar room and to provide laboratory space and accommodation for scientific staff. Both forward drive diesels were removed to make room for electronic equipment and auxiliaries, and to provide crew accommodation. Sonar test equipment was replaced during each reconstruction phase. In 1968 *Grouper* was discarded, her role being taken over by *Tigrone* (AGSS-419).

From 1960 to 1968 *Archerfish* (AGSS-311) acted as an oceanographic research vessel. Her conversion was funded in Fiscal Year 1960, and was completed in the same year. All torpedo tubes were removed to make room for laboratory equipment and to provide additional accommodation space. It has been recorded that, because she made such long sea trips, *Archerfish* had an all-bachelor crew. Unlike many conversions, *Archerfish* was left with her entire powerplant and reduction gearing intact, and external modifications were so slight that it is difficult to distinguish her from other fleet submarines.

Finally, we have *Tigrone*, converted after many years' service as a radar submarine. She was reclassified SS-419 at the beginning of 1961, and became an AGSS at the end of 1963 with her reconstruction as a sonar test submarine for the Naval Underwater Sound Laboratory, and then, from 1968, as the successor to *Grouper* (AGSS-214). *Tigrone* was easy to identify from her external appearance, partly from her typical conning tower, but mainly by the large drum-like sonar bulge housing a soundproof sonar room installed in the bows. All torpedo tubes were removed. *Tigrone* served as a sonar test boat for eleven years, until 1975.

Special Conversion AGSS-299

| Pennant numbers | Ships in the class | | displacement surfaced | Dimensions m | | | Output HP | Speed kn | Range Sm/kn | Oil fuel ts | Comple- ment | Original combat systems |
AGSS	plan- ned	com- pleted	submerged	length	beam	draught					Officers/ enlisted	
299	1	1	1790	95,2	8,3		2305	14				6 bow, 4 stern torpedo tubes 21in (sealed off)
	aus FY 49		2400					9				

Powerplant: as *Balao* Class, but with
2 generator diesels removed

Balao type, in post-War AGSS configuration.

Special Conversion AGSS-318

| Pennant numbers | Ships in the class | | displacement surfaced | Dimensions m | | | Output HP | Speed kn | Range Sm/kn | Oil fuel ts | Comple- ment | Original combat systems |
AGSS	plan- ned	com- pleted	submerged	length	beam	draught					Officers/ enlisted	
318	1	1	1959: 2220	zuerst: 95,2	8,3		3430	10,5			~ 11/70	All tubes removed
	aus den FY 49 bis FY 72		2600	nach Verlängerung: 100,7	8,3		2740	8				

Powerplant: direct diesel-electric;
gearing and 1 main generator diesel
removed; 2 main diesels.

Special Conversion AGSS-214

| Pennant numbers | Ships in the class | | displacement surfaced | Dimensions m | | | Output HP | Speed kn | Range Sm/kn | Oil fuel ts | Comple- ment | Original combat systems |
AGSS	plan- ned	com- pleted	submerged	length	beam	draught					Officers/ enlisted	
214	1	1	2055	93,3	8,3		2400	15			~ 7/74	4 Stern-TR 21in (sealed off)
	aus den FY 58 bis FY 68		2400				2740	9				

Powerplant: *see* following SSK-214

Special Conversion AGSS-311

Pennant numbers	Ships in the class		displacement surfaced	Dimensions m			Output HP	Speed kn	Range Sm/kn	Oil fuel ts	Comple- ment	Original combat systems
AGSS	plan- ned	com- pleted	submerged	length	beam	draught					Officers/ enlisted	
311	1	1	2040	95,2	8,3		5400	18			~ 10/72	Torpedo tubes removed
	aus FY 60		2400				2740	9				

Powerplant: *see Balao* Class

Special Conversion AGSS-419

Pennant numbers	Ships in the class		displacement surfaced	Dimensions m			Output HP	Speed kn	Range Sm/kn	Oil fuel ts	Comple- ment	Original combat systems
AGSS	plan- ned	com- pleted	submerged	length	beam	draught					Officers/ enlisted	
419	1	1	1990	93,2	8,3		4610	18			~ 11/65	Torpedo tubes removed
	aus FY 63		2410					9				

Powerplant: *see SSR-419*

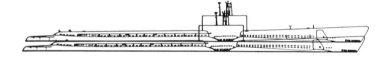

Flying Fish as AGSS, with sonar equipment around the conning tower.

Manta (AGSS-299) in 1967, shortly before the end of her service as a training hulk for the NRF. In this condition she lies high in the water; her propellers have been removed. She still carries the flag because she is considered 'out of commission, in service'. [INRO])

Baya (AGSS-318) on 5 August 1959, without deck armament but already with rounded sonar bow. [LvG]

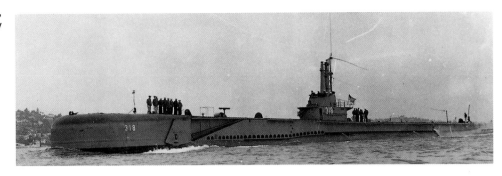

Baya in 1959, now with the huge LORAD (Long Range Active Detection System) drum aft of the conning tower. [AB])

This later photograph shows more clearly the rounded sonar bow of *Baya* and the altered forward part of the conning tower design. [USN]

Flying Fish (AGSS-229) in 1957, after installation of conning tower-mounted passive sonar equipment. [USN]

This photograph of *Flying Fish*, probably taken at the same time, shows the size of the sonar drum. [AB]

189

Grouper (AGSS-214) in December 1961, with research apparatus on deck. The unfriendly message below her pennant number is an indication of the rivalry between the services; in this case it refers to a forthcoming sporting event. [USN]

Tigrone (AGSS-419), off Groton, Connecticut in 1970. The 'cap-feather' aerial on the conning tower can be clearly seen. [LvG]

A somewhat later photograph shows *Tigrone* in British waters. She has her original conning tower, but the huge bow sonar dome is a notable addition. As she took over the duties of *Grouper* in 1968, the BRASS system billboard array was fitted, and can be seen here aft of the conning tower. Note that in the first edition of DICNAVAB (1970) (*see* Bibliography) the abbreviation BRASS does not occur. In the third edition (1986), the following definition is given: 'Ballistic Range for Aircraft Survivability Studies'. It must however be assumed that this has nothing to do with the system installed in *Tigrone*.

ASW Submarine Conversions (SSK)

Very shortly after the end of the War it became apparent that, because of the fundamental advances in underwater technology, submarine-to-submarine combat would become inevitable. As a result of developments based on the latest U-boats, it had become possible for submarines to outrun surface pursuers. Moreover, with their inadequate listening apparatus, destroyers, frigates, corvettes and other submarine-chasers would soon lose track of such fast vessels. This generated an immediate need to be able to locate submarines under water at great distances, and led to the concept of the 'hunter-killer sub-marine'. The theory was that these vessels would lie in wait outside enemy harbours so as to locate, follow and destroy enemy submarines passing in or out. To achieve this hunter-killers (SSK) would need:

- a high degree of silencing;
- newer, long-range sonars;
- new anti-submarine homing torpedoes.

This was a whole new philosophy of submarine warfare. Previously, submarines had engaged surface vessels, especially merchant ships, but now they would have to take on other submarines, although of course using different methods. The reader may recall that this idea was behind the design of the K-1 boats. The last example of this type was the one-off nuclear submarine *Tullibee* (SSN-597).

At that time there were two models for the conversion of fleet submarines to SSKs. The first was *Grouper* (SS-214) which was reclassified SSK at the beginning of 1951; this was a test conversion before more boats were rebuilt to a later specification, Model II. *Grouper* was fitted with a snorkel and a GUPPY-type conning tower, but around the forward edge of the conning tower was a semi-circular array of hydrophones for the BQR-3 sonar. Both forward drive units were removed, and the auxiliaries were extensively silenced.

Next, a Model II conversion was carried out on six *Gato*-Class boats from 1952, based on the experience with *Grouper*. Both upper forward torpedo tubes were removed, and a bow sonar room, containing a semi-circular array of BQR-4A hydrophones, was installed. The bow sonar dome and the specially shaped conning tower make these vessels easily recognizable. The foreship sloped gently upwards towards the bows, ending in the large rounded dome, which had plastics 'windows' to facilitate tracking performance. Beam-on photographs give the impression that the rounded bows fell away steeply, an impression that remained even after the SSKs had been returned to 'SS' status in 1959.

One main and one auxiliary drive unit were removed, and the old electric motors were exchanged for newer, slower-running units. To reduce noise, the deck edges were streamlined, and great attention was paid to soundproofing the interior. The new drive units were already relatively quiet, but the engine mountings were changed and piping insulated, so that a minimum of vibration was transmitted to the surrounding sea.

From 1959 it became clear that the existing hunter-killer concept was becoming increasingly outdated in view of the advent of high-speed nuclear submarines. Soon afterwards the SSNs took over the entire anti-submarine function, including sub-hunting, hence the extended name 'hunter-killer'. Their higher speed, better hull-form, greater operational depth and silent running made them much more suited to the task. Finally came the introduction of the new generation of anti-submarine missiles such as SUBROC, which signalled the end of the fleet submarine conversions.

SSK Conversions

PN	Name	Original-Class	In Service	Shipyard	Conversion Complete
214	*Grouper*	Gato	42	MI	51
240	*Angler*	Gato	43	EB	53
241	*Bashaw*	Gato	43	SF	53
242	*Bluegill*	Gato	43	SF	53
243	*Bream*	Gato	44	SF	53
244	*Cavalla*	Gato	44	EB	53
246	*Croaker*	Gato	44	Pts	53

SSK Model II, *Angler* Class.

Killer Submarine Conversion SSK-214

Pennant numbers	Ships in the class		displacement surfaced	Dimensions m			Output HP	Speed kn	Range Sm/kn	Oil fuel ts	Complement	Original combat systems
SSK	planned	completed	submerged	length	beam	draught					Officers/enlisted	
214	1	1	2055	93,3	8,3		2400	15			~ 7/74	4 bow, 4 stern Torpedo tubes 21in
	aus FY 50		2400				2740	9				

Powerplant: direct diesel-electric;
gearing and 2 main generator
diesels removed.

Hunter-Killer Conversion SSK-240-Class

Pennant numbers SSK	Ships in the class		displacement surfaced submerged	Dimensions m			Output HP	Speed kn	Range Sm/kn	Oil fuel ts	Complement Officers/ enlisted	Original combat systems
	planned	completed		length	beam	draught						
240 – 244 246	6 aus FY 52	6	2070 2400	93,5	8,3		3800 2740	17 9			~ 7/74	4 bow, 4 stern Torpedo tubes 21in

Powerplant: Direct diesel-electric; gearing and 1 main and 1 auxiliary   generator diesel removed ; two main drive diesels.

When this 1961 photograph of *Grouper* was taken she had been AGSS for some time (*see* e.g., the BRASS equipment aft of the conning tower). However, a relic of her SSK days can be clearly seen: the BQR-3 sonar equipment on the conning tower leading edge. [AB]

Ten months after decommissioning: *Angler* (ex-SSK-240, ex-SS-240, ex-AGSS-240, ex-IXSS-240) seen on 25 October 1972. The bow sonar dome for BQR-4A is clearly visible. [LvG]) ▼

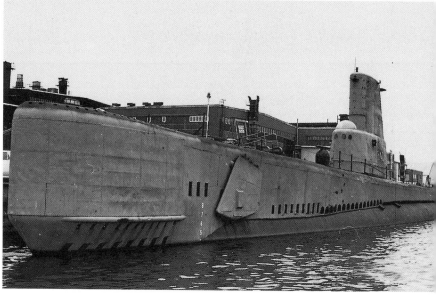

This rather out-of-focus shot of *Bashaw* (SSK-241) does show the leading edge of the BQR-4A sonar dome. Note the plastics 'windows'. [AB]

Bow and stern views of *Bream* (SSK-243), seen off San Francisco after a refit, 7 February 1956. [USN]

Bluegill (SSK-242) carrying out speed trials in San Francisco Bay on 23 July 1953, immediately after her special-purpose conversion. All SSKs were fitted with the hydro-dynamic GUPPY conning tower. [USN]

Bream (SSK-243) in 1953. [USN]

Fourteen years after the above photograph was taken *Bluegill*, now (1967) classified AGSS-242, shows one external difference from the GUPPY boats: the long, flat foreship. [USN]

Undated photograph of *Cavalla* (SSK-244). [USN]

Undated photograph of *Croaker* (SSK-246). [USN]

Some seventeen years after having been stricken, the four-times re-classified *Croaker* is seen in 1988 at NISMF Norfolk, alongside the equally long-retired guided missile cruiser *Albany* (ex-CG-10). [1 October 1988, Te; 7 July 1988,WD]

195

Administrative Reclassifications

AGSS Reclassification

Apart from the specialized AGSS conversions described above, a great many fleet submarines of various designations were reclassified AGSS from 1950 to 1969. In these cases the AGSS designation indicated that the boat, while remaining on active service, had been allocated to training or other non-active duty. Confusingly, this did not mean that the vessel could not occasionally carry out normal fleet submarine duties. From 1962 some boats in the reserve were reclassified AGSS, as were some NRT units, indicating that they were no longer considered fit for combat. In these cases the AGSS classification did not in any way indicate that any modifications had been carried out.

Administrative AGSS-Reclassification

PN	Name	AGSS from	Previous Classi-fication	Status	Notes
362	Guavina	11. 12. 51	SSO	active	reclassi-fied as AOSS 22.6.57
274	Rock	31. 12. 59	SSR	active	
285	Balao	1. 4. 60	SS	active	
291	Crevalle	1. 4. 60	SS	active	
435	Corsair	1. 4. 60	SS	active	
269	Rasher	1. 7. 60	SSR	active	
270	Raton	1. 7. 60	SSR	active	
309	Aspro	1. 7. 60	SS	active	
336	Capitaine	1. 7. 60	SS	active	
393	Queenfish	1. 7. 60	SS	active	
395	Redfish	1. 7. 60	SS	active	
400	Sea Devil	1. 7. 60	SS	active	
477	Conger	9. 3. 62	SS	active	
404	Spikefish	1. 7. 62	SS	active	
422	Toro	1. 7. 62	SS	active	
479	Diablo	1. 7. 62	SS	active	
488	Sarda	1. 7. 62	SS	active	
241	Bashaw	1. 9. 62	SS, ex-SSK	active	
224	Cod	1. 12. 62	SS	NRT	
225	Cero	1. 12. 62	SS	NRT	
228	Drum	1. 12. 62	SS	NRT	
236	Silversides	1. 12. 62	SS	NRT	
245	Cobia	1. 12. 62	SS	NRT	
256	Hake	1. 12. 62	SS	NRT	
286	Billfish	1. 12. 62	SS	NRT	
287	Bowfin	1. 12. 62	SS	NRT	
288	Cabrilla	1. 12. 62	SS	NRT	
292	Devilfish	1. 12. 62	SS	ResFlt	
295	Hackleback	1. 12. 62	SS	ResFlt	

PN	Name	AGSS from	Previous Classi-fication	Status	Notes
297	Ling	1. 12. 62	SS	NRT	
298	Lionfish	1. 12. 62	SS	NRT	
300	Moray	1. 12. 62	SS	ResFlt	
301	Roncador	1. 12. 62	SS	NRT	
304	Seahorse	1. 12. 62	SS	ResFlt	
310	Batfish	1. 12. 62	SS	NRT	
321	Besugo	1. 12. 62	SS	ResFlt	
334	Cabezon	1. 12. 62	SS	NRT	
335	Dentuda	1. 12. 62	SS	NRT	
374	Loggerhead	1. 12. 62	SS	NRT	
383	Pampanito	1. 12. 62	SS	NRT	
384	Parche	1. 12. 62	SS	NRT	
387	Pintado	1. 12. 62	SS	ResFlt	
388	Pipefish	1. 12. 62	SS	ResFlt	
389	Piranha	1. 12. 62	SS	ResFlt	
401	Sea Dog	1. 12. 62	SS	NRT	
411	Spadefish	1. 12. 62	SS	ResFlt	
412	Trepang	1. 12. 62	SS	NRT	
272	Redfin	28. 6. 63	SS, ex-SSR	active	
240	Angler	1. 7. 63	SS, ex-SSK	active	
244	Cavalla	1. 7. 63	SS, ex-SSK	active	
243	Bream	13. 4. 65	SS, ex-SSK	active	
242	Bluegill	1. 4. 66	SS, ex-SSK	active	
328	Charr	1. 7. 66	SS (FS)	active	
246	Croaker	1. 5. 67	SS, ex-SSK	active	
480	Medregal	1. 5. 67	SS (FS)	active	recl. as SS 1.10.69
338	Carp	1. 5. 68	SS (FS) NRT		
423	Torsk	1. 5. 68	SS (FS) NRT		
399	Sea Cat	29. 6. 68	SS (FS)	active	twice as AGSS
481	Requin	29. 6. 68	SS, ex-SSR	active	
476	Runner	1. 2. 69	SS (FS)	active	
409	Piper	15. 6. 69	SS (FS)	active	
303	Sablefish	30. 6. 69	SS (FS)	active	
331	Bugara	30. 6. 69	SS (FS)	active	recl. as SS 1.10.69
337	Carbonero	30. 6. 69	SS (FS)	active	recl. as SS 1.10.69
348	Cusk	30. 6. 69	SS (FS) ex-SSG	active	
405	Sea Owl	30. 6. 69	SS (FS)	active	
482	Irex	30. 6. 69	SS (FS)	active	
489	Spinax	30. 6. 69	SS, ex-SSR	active	
342	Chopper	15. 9. 69	SS (GIA)	NRT	
319	Becuna	1. 10. 69	SS (GIA)	active	recl. as SS 30.6.71
324	Blenny	1. 10. 69	SS (GIA)	active	recl. as SS 30.6.71
403	Atule	1. 10. 69	SS (GIA)	active	recl. as SS 30.6.71
417	Tench	1. 10. 69	SS (GIA)	active	recl. as SS 30.6.71
406	Sea Poacher	1. 11. 69	SS (GIA)	active	recl. as SS 30.6.71

IXSS Classification

In mid-1971 there were still ten submarines in use as 'training hulks' – that is, immobilized dockside hulls used for static training purposes. The Navy decided that it was not appropriate for these craft to carry the same designation as boats that were still capable of service, and so the new category 'miscellaneous unclassified submarine' (IXSS) was created. Only *Perch* was transferred from the LPSS category; all others had been AGSS.

Administrative IXSS-Reclassifications

PN	Name	IXSS from	Previous Classification	Status
224	Cod	30. 6. 71	AGSS	NRT
287	Bowfin	30. 6. 71	AGSS	NRT
297	Ling	30. 6. 71	AGSS	NRT
298	Lionfish	30. 6. 71	AGSS	NRT
301	Roncador	30. 6. 71	AGSS	NRT
313	Perch	30. 6. 71	LPSS	NRT
338	Carp	30. 6. 71	AGSS	NRT
342	Chopper	30. 6. 71	AGSS	NRT
383	Pampanito	30. 6. 71	AGSS	NRT
423	Torsk	30. 6. 71	AGSS	NRT

Transfer of US Submarines to Foreign Navies

As with other types of ship in 1945, surplus submarines were not only scrapped or transferred to the reserve, but were in some cases transferred to the navies of friendly nations. This also happened under the auspices of various naval support programs, the significance of which is explained in my book *Destroyers of the US Navy*, pp. 273-4.

Both the following summaries were prepared by Manfred Reinert.

Transfer of US Submarines to Foreign Navies

Pennant No. SS-	Name	Date of Transfer	to	New Name
Gato Class				
220	Barb	13. 12. 54	Italy	Enrico Tazzoli
247	Dace	31. 1. 55	Italy	Leonardo da Vinci
259	Jack	21. 4. 58	Greece	Amphitriti
260	Lapon	10. 8. 57	Greece	Poseidon
261	Mingo	15. 8. 55	Japan	Kuroshio
262	Muskallunge	18. 1. 57	Brazil	Humaita
263	Paddle	18. 1. 57	Brazil	Riachuelo
363	Guitarro	7. 8. 54	Turkey	Preveze
364	Hammerhead	23. 10. 54	Turkey	Cerbe
Balao Class				
307	Tilefish	4. 5. 60	Venezuela	Carite
312	Burrfish	11. 5. 61	Canada	Grilse
320	Bergall	18. 10. 58	Turkey	Turgut Reis
321	Besugo	31. 3. 66	Italy	Francesco Morosini
323	Caiman	30. 6. 72	Turkey	Dumlupinar
325	Blower	16. 11. 50	Turkey	Dumlupinar
326	Blueback	23. 5. 48	Turkey	Ikinci Inönu
327	Boarfish	23. 5. 48	Turkey	Sakarya
329	Chub	25. 5. 48	Turkey	Gur
330	Brill	23. 5. 48	Turkey	Birinci Inönu
333	Bumper	16. 11. 50	Turkey	Canakkale

Pennant No. SS-	Name	Date of Transfer	to	New Name
336	*Capitaine*	5. 3. 66	Italy	*Alfredo Cappellini*
339	*Catfish*	1. 7. 71	Argentina	*Santa Fe*
340	*Entemedor*	31. 7. 72	Turkey	*Preveze*
341	*Chivo*	1. 7. 71	Argentina	*Santiago del Estero*
344	*Cobbler*	21. 11. 73	Turkey	*Canakkale*
346	*Corporal*	21. 11. 73	Turkey	*Birinci Inönu*
347	*Cubera*	5. 1. 72	Venezuela	*Tiburon*
350	*Dogfish*	28. 7. 72	Brazil	*Guanabara*
351	*Greenfish*	19. 12. 73	Brazil	*Amazonas*
365	*Hardhead*	26. 7. 72	Greece	*Papanikolis*
366	*Hawkbill*	21. 4. 53	Netherlands	*Zeeleuw*
367	*Icefish*	21. 2. 53	Netherlands	*Walrus*
368	*Jallao*	26. 6. 74	Spain	
370	Kraken	24. 10. 59	Spain	*Almirante Garcia de Los Reyes*
372	*Lamprey*	21. 8. 60	Argentina	*Santa Fe*
373	*Lizardfish*	9. 1. 60	Italy	*Evangelista Torricelli*
375	*Macabi*	11. 8. 60	Argentina	*Santiago del Estero*
376	*Mapiro*	18. 3. 60	Turkey	*Piri Reis*
378	*Mero*	20. 4. 60	Turkey	*Hizir Reis*
381	*Sand Lance*	7. 9. 63	Brazil	*Rio Grande do Sul*
382	*Picuda*	1. 10. 72	Spain	*Narciso Monturiol*
385	*Bang*	1. 10. 72	Spain	*Cosme Garcia*
390	*Plaice*	7. 9. 63	Brazil	*Bahia*
391	*Pomfret*	1. 7. 71	Turkey	*Oruc Reis*
394	*Razorback*	30. 11. 70	Turkey	*Murat Reis*
396	*Ronquil*	1. 7. 71	Spain	*Isaac Peral*
397	*Scabbardfish*	26. 2. 65	Greece	*Triaina*
402	*Sea Fox*	14. 12. 70	Turkey	*Burak Reis*
403	*Atule*	31. 7. 74	Peru	*Pacocha*
406	*Sea Poacher*	1. 7. 74	Peru	*Pabellon de Pica/La Pedrera*
410	*Threadfin*	18. 8. 72	Turkey	*Ikinci Inönu*
413	*Spot*	12. 1. 62	Chile	*Simpson*
414	*Springer*	23. 1. 61	Chile	*Thomson*
425	*Trumpetfish*	15. 10. 73	Brazil	*Goias*
426	*Tusk*	18. 10. 73	Taiwan	*Hai Pao*

Tench-Class

Pennant No. SS-	Name	Date of Transfer	to	New Name
417	*Tench*	16. 9. 76	Peru	C
418	*Thornback*	1. 7. 71	Turkey	*Uluc Ali Reis*
421	*Trutta*	1. 7. 72	Turkey	*Cerbe*
475	*Argonaut*	2. 12. 68	Canada	*Rainbow*
478	*Cutlass*	12. 4. 73	Taiwan	*Hai Shih*
479	*Diablo*	1. 6. 64	Pakistan	*Ghazi*
483	*Sea Leopard*	27. 3. 73	Brazil	*Bahia*
484	*Odax*	8. 7. 72	Brazil	*Rio de Janeiro*
487	*Remora*	29. 10. 73	Greece	*Katsonis*
490	*Volador*	18. 8. 72	Italy	*Gianfranco Gazzana Priaroggia*
522	*Amberjack*	17. 10. 73	Brazil	*Ceara*
523	*Grampus*	13. 5. 72	Brazil	*Rio Grande do Sul*
524	*Pickerel*	18. 8. 72	Italy	*Primo Longobardo*
525	*Grenadier*	15. 5. 73	Venezuela	*Picua*

Tang-Class

Pennant No. SS-	Name	Date of Transfer	to	New Name
563	*Tang*	2. 80	Turkey	*Piri Reis*
564	*Trigger*	10. 7. 73	Italy	*Livio Piomarta*
567	*Gudgeon*	9. 83	Turkey	*Hizir Reis*
568	*Harder*	20. 2. 74	Italy	*Romeo Romei*

Summary of US Submarines Transferred, by Country of Destination

Argen-tina	Brazil	Chile	Greece	Italy	Japan	Canada	Nether-lands	Pakistan	Peru	Spain	Taiwan	Turkey	Vene-zuela
339	262	413	259	220	261	312	366	479	403	368	426	320	307
341	263	414	260	247		475	367		406	370	478	323	347
372	350		365	321					417	382		325	525
375	351		397	336						385		326	
	381		487	373						396		327	
	390			490								329	
	425			524								330	
	483			564								333	
	484			568								340	
	522											344	
	523											346	
												363	
												364	
												376	
												378	
												391	
												394	
												402	
												410	
												418	
												421	
												563	
												567	
4	11	2	5	9	1	2	2	1	3	5	2	23	3

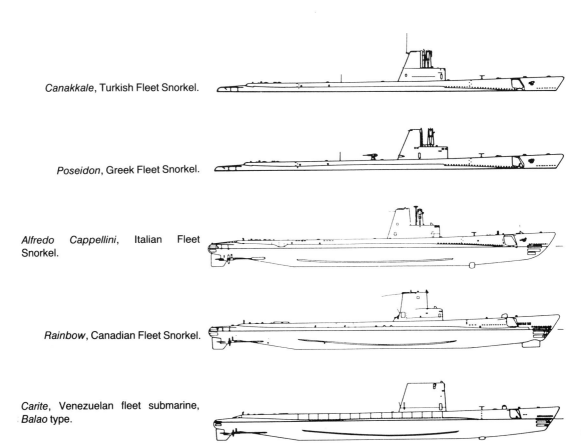

Canakkale, Turkish Fleet Snorkel.

Poseidon, Greek Fleet Snorkel.

Alfredo Cappellini, Italian Fleet Snorkel.

Rainbow, Canadian Fleet Snorkel.

Carite, Venezuelan fleet submarine, *Balao* type.

Caiman (ex-SS-323), now *Dumlupinar* of the Turkish Navy, seen off Istanbul, 9 August 1962. At this time she had already served in the Turkish Navy for ten years. [LvG])

From 1966 to 1977 *Capitaine* (ex-SS-336) became *Alfredo Cappellini* (S 507) of the Italian Navy. It is interesting to note the semi-clad tower, the significance of which has never been discussed in the technical press. The pennant number has suffered obvious weather damage.

In 1972 *Hardhead* (ex-SS-365) was transferred to Greece, where she was renamed *Papanikolis* and given the NATO number S 114. She is seen here in July 1979. [LvG]

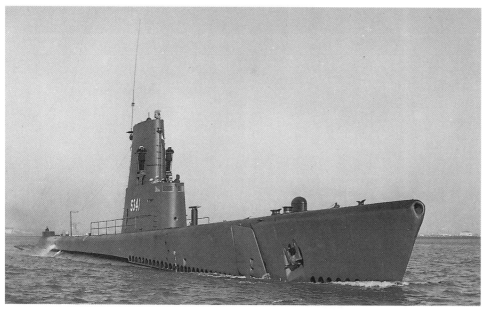

Another transfer to the Turkish Navy was *Hammerhead* (ex-SS-364), which became *Cerbe* and received the NATO number S 341. Photographed *circa* December 1960.

The Argentine Navy took over *Macabi* (ex-SS-375) in 1960 and renamed her *Santiago del Estero*; she was transferred without deck armament.

This photograph taken off Thessaloniki in September 1979 shows *Remora* (ex-SS-487), one of the GUPPY III boats, in her new guise of *Katsonis* (S 115) of the Greek Navy. [LvG])

From 1972 *Pickerel* (ex-SS-524) became *Primo Longobardo* (S 501) of the Italian Navy. This sad photograph shows this GUPPY III boat on her last voyage to the breakers. [LG]

The former *Harder* (ex-SS-568) became an Italian boat in 1974 and was given the name *Romeo Romei* and the NATO designation S 516.

201

Naval Reserve Force Submarines

Because of the number of surplus submarines available at the end of the War, the US Navy was able to carry out an extensive training programme for reservists over the next two decades. For this reason, therefore, numerous fleet submarines were transferred to the Naval Reserve Force (NRF) from 1947 onwards, most having first been disarmed. They were moored as dockside training hulks in ports with NRF bases, replacing older training boats which were fit only for the breaker's yard. During their service as training hulks, these boats were classified AGSS, although, as we have seen in the previous Section, it was eventually decided, on 30 June 1971, to classify the last ten training hulks IXSS to distinguish them from active AGSS units.

When the last active fleet submarines were discarded there was no longer any need to train reservists. No attempt had been made to set up reserve training units for nuclear submarines, probably because their highly technical nature precluded the use of reservists even in emergencies. Training of active crews took place on land, where simulators played a useful role.

However, something like the old NRF hulks staged a late re-appearance at the beginning of the 1990s. At great expense, three old SSBNs, redundant as a result of arms control agreements, have been converted to stationary hulks for the training of active nuclear submarine crew. After conversion, they were given the new designation ARTB: *Daniel Webster* (ex-SSBN-629) became ARTB-1, and *Sam Rayburn* (ex-SSBN-635) ARTB-2. It is probable that a third SSBN is to be modified as a training hulk during Fiscal Year 1992.

The following survey covers the mass of fleet submarines that served from 1946 to 1971 as NRF training boats, and is arranged in ascending order of pennant number.

Naval Reserve for Submarines

Pennant No	Name	Type	NRF-Service	Category	Base
SS-172	*Porpoise*	*Porpoise*	8. 5. 47 – 2. 56	SS	Houston, Texas
SS-173	*Pike*	*Porpoise*	31. 7. 47 – 17. 2. 56	SS	Baltimore, Maryland
SS-175	*Tarpon*	*Shark*	17. 4. 47 – 5. 9. 56	SS	New Orleans, Louisiana
SS-178	*Permit*	*Perch*	24. 1. 47 – 56	SS	Philadelphia, Pennsylvania
SS-179	*Plunger*	*Perch*	5. 46 – 2. 54	SS	Brooklyn, NY, 1946–1952; Jacksonville, FL, 1952–1954
SS-183	*Seal*	*Salmon*	19. 6. 47 – 56	SS	Boston, Massachusetts
SS-198	*Tambor*	*Tambor*	2. 4. 47 – 1. 9. 59	SS	Detroit, Michigan
SS-199	*Tautog*	*Tambor*	4. 47 – 1. 9. 59	SS	Milwaukee, Wisconsin
SS-206	*Gar*	*Tambor*	4. 47 – 1. 8. 59	SS	Cleveland, Ohio
SS-212	*Gato*	*Gato*	52 – 1. 3. 60	SS	Brooklyn, NY, 1952–1956; Baltimore, MD, 1956–1960
SS-213	*Greenling*	*Gato*	12. 46 – 1. 3. 60	SS	Portsmouth, New Hampshire
SS-217	*Guardfish*	*Gato*	18. 6. 48 – 1. 6. 60	SS	New London, Connecticut
SS-221	*Blackfish*	*Gato*	5. 5. 49 – 19. 5. 54	SS	St. Petersburg, Florida
SS-224	*Cod*	*Gato*	1. 5. 60 – 15. 12. 71	IXSS	Cleveland, Ohio
SS-225	*Cero*	*Gato*	12. 9. 59 – 30. 6. 67	AGSS	Detroit, Michigan
SS-228	*Drum*	*Gato*	18. 3. 47 – 30. 6. 68	AGSS	Washington, District of Columbia

Pennant No	Name	Type	NRF Service	Category	Base
SS-231	Haddock	Gato	8. 48 – 5. 52	SS	Jacksonville, FL, 1948–1952;
			und 6. 56 – 60	SS	Boston, MA, 1956–1960
SS-234	Kingfish	Gato	6. 10. 47 – 1. 3. 60	SS	Providence, Rhode Island
SS-235	Shad	Gato	10. 47 – 1. 4. 60	SS	Beverly, MA, 1947–1948;
					Salem, MA, 1948–1960
SS-236	Silversides	Gato	15. 10. 47 – 30. 6. 69	AGSS	Chicago, Illinois
SS-239	Whale	Gato	22. 1. 57 – 60	SS	New Orleans, Louisiana
SS-240	Angler	Gato	1. 4. 68 – 15. 12. 71	IXSS	Philadelphia, Pennsylvania
SS-244	Cavalla	Gato	30. 6. 68 – 30. 12. 69	AGSS	Houston, Texas
SS-245	Cobia	Gato	12. 9. 59 – 1. 7. 70	AGSS	Milwaukee, Wisconsin
SS-246	Croaker	Gato	2. 4. 68 – 20. 12. 71	IXSS	Portsmouth, New Hampshire
SS-254	Gurnard	Gato	4. 49 – 6. 60	SS	Pearl Harbor, HI, 1949–1953;
					Tacoma, WA, 1953–1960
SS-256	Hake	Gato	15. 10. 56 – 19. 4. 68	AGSS	Philadelphia, Pennsylvania
SS-258	Hoe	Gato	9. 56 – 15. 4. 60	SS	Brooklyn, New York
SS-264	Pargo	Gato	12. 6. 46 – 1. 12. 60	SS	Portland, Oregon
SS-265	Peto	Gato	11. 56 – 1. 8. 60	SS	Houston, Texas
SS-268	Puffer	Gato	46 – 10. 6. 60	SS	Seattle, Washington
SS-269	Rasher	Gato	27. 5. 67 – 20. 12. 71	IXSS	Portland, Oregon
SS-272	Redfin	Gato	30. 6. 67 – 1. 7. 70	AGSS	Baltimore, Maryland
SS-276	Sawfish	Gato	15. 5. 47 – 1. 4. 60	SS	San Pedro, California
SS-280	Steelhead	Gato	12. 11. 47 – 1. 4. 60	SS	San Diego, California
SS-281	Sunfish	Gato	4. 49 – 1. 5. 60	SS	Vallejo, California
SS-286	Billfish	Balao	1. 1. 60 – 1. 4. 68	AGSS	Boston, Massachusetts
SS-287	Bowfin	Balao	10. 6. 60 – 1. 12. 71	IXSS	Seattle, Washington
SS-288	Cabrilla	Balao	5. 60 – 30. 6. 68	AGSS	Houston, Texas
SS-291	Crevalle	Balao	62 – 68	AGSS	Portsmouth, New Hampshire
SS-297	Ling	Balao	3. 60 – 1. 12. 71	IXSS	Brooklyn, New York
SS-298	Lionfish	Balao	1. 3. 60 – 20. 12. 71	IXSS	Providence, Rhode Island
SS-299	Manta	Balao	4. 60 – 30. 6. 67	AGSS	New London, Connecticut
SS-301	Roncador	Balao	2. 60 – 1. 12. 71	IXSS	San Pedro, California
SS-310	Batfish	Balao	1. 60 – 1. 11. 69	AGSS	New Orleans, Louisiana
SS-313	Perch	Balao	30. 6. 67 – 1. 12. 71	IXSS	San Diego, California
SS-315	Sealion	Balao	30. 6. 60 – 28. 8. 61	APSS	Portsmouth, New Hampshire
SS-328	Charr	Balao	28. 6. 69 – 20. 12. 71	IXSS	Alameda, California
SS-334	Cabezon	Balao	4. 60 – 15. 5. 70	AGSS	Tacoma, Washington
SS-335	Dentuda	Balao	11. 12. 46 – 30. 6. 67	AGSS	San Francisco, California
SS-338	Carp	Balao	18. 3. 68 – 20. 12. 71	IXSS	Boston, Massachusetts
SS-342	Chopper	Balao	27. 8. 69 – 1. 10. 71	IXSS	New Orleans, Louisiana
SS-362	Guavina	Gato	2. 60 – 30. 6. 67	AOSS	Baltimore, Maryland
SS-374	Loggerhead	Balao	1. 6. 60 – 30. 6. 67	AGSS	Portland, Oregon
SS-383	Pampanito	Balao	4. 60 – 20. 12. 71	IXSS	Vallejo, California
SS-384	Parche	Balao	10. 2. 48 – 8. 11. 69	AGSS	Alameda, California
SS-401	Sea Dog	Balao	2. 60 – 2. 12. 68	AGSS	Salem, Massachusetts
SS-409	Piper	Balao	16. 6. 67 – 1. 7. 70	AGSS	Detroit, Michigan
SS-412	Trepang	Balao	2. 60 – 30. 6. 67	AGSS	San Diego, California
SS-423	Torsk	Tench	4. 3. 68 – 15. 12. 71	IXSS	Washington, District of Columbia
SS-476	Runner	Tench	29. 6. 70 – 15. 12. 71	IXSS	Chicago, Illinois
SS-481	Requin	Tench	2. 69 – 20. 12. 71	IXSS	St. Petersburg, Florida

Submarine Losses during the Second World War

During the War, the Navy lost a total of 52 submarines in action or as a result of error, stranding, collision or other mishap. The following review, compiled by Manfred Reinert, is arranged in ascending order of pennant number.

Submarine Losses in the Second World War

Pennant No	Name	Date	Course and Location
SS-89	R 12	12. 6. 43	During training off east coast of USA
SS-131	S 26	24. 1. 42	Collision with PC-460 off Panama
SS-132	S 27	19. 6. 42	Stranding off Amchitka Island
SS-133	S 28	4. 7. 44	During training after accident off Hawaii
SS-141	S 36	20. 1. 42	Stranding in Makassar Straits
SS-144	S 39	14. 8. 42	Stranding off Rossell Island
SS-155	S 44	7. 10. 43	Japanese destroyer off Paramushiru, Kuriles
SS-166	Argonaut	10. 1. 43	Japanese destroyer off New Britain
SS-174	Shark	2. 42	Japanese naval forces off Menado, Celebes
SS-176	Perch	3. 3. 42	Japanese destroyer in Java Sea
SS-177	Pickerel	3. 4. 43	Japanese naval forces north of Honshu, Japan
SS-181	Pompano	9. 43	Japanese mine north of Honshu, Japan
SS-191	Sculpin	19. 11. 43	Japanese destroyer off Truk
SS-193	Swordfish	12. 1. 45	Japanese naval forces off Okinawa
SS-195	Sealion	25. 12. 41	Japanese aircraft off Cavite, Philippines
SS-197	Seawolf	3. 10. 44	Sunk by USS Richard M. Rowell (DE-403) off Morotai
SS-201	Triton	15. 3. 43	Japanese destroyer north of Admiralty Islands
SS-202	Trout	29. 2. 44	Japanese naval forces north-west of the Philippines
SS-207	Grampus	3. 43	Japanese destroyer in the Blackett Strait
SS-208	Grayback	27. 2. 44	Japanese aircraft south of Okinawa
SS-209	Grayling	9. 43	Japanese cargo vessel off Manila
SS-210	Grenadier	21. 4. 43	Japanese aircraft off Penang, Malaya
SS-211	Gudgeon	18. 4. 44	Japanese aircraft off Maug Island, Marianas
SS-215	Growler	8. 11. 44	Japanese naval forces west of the Philippines
SS-216	Grunion	7. 42	Sunk off Kiska, cause unknown
SS-218	Albacore	7. 11. 44	Japanese mine north of Hokkaido, Japan
SS-219	Amberjack	2. 43	Japanese torpedo boat off Rabaul
SS-223	Bonefish	18. 6. 45	Japanese naval forces in Toyama Bay, Japan
SS-226	Corvina	16. 11. 43	Japanese submarine south of Truk
SS-227	Darter	24. 10. 44	Sunk by US naval forces after stranding off Palawan
SS-233	Herring	1. 6. 44	Japanese coastal artillery off Matsuwa, Kuriles
SS-237	Trigger	28. 3. 45	Japanese naval and air forces in East China Sea
SS-238	Wahoo	11. 10. 43	Japanese aircraft in La Perouse Strait
SS-248	Dorado	12. 10. 43	Sunk by US aircraft en route to Panama
SS-250	Flier	13. 8. 44	Japanese mine in Balabac Strait
SS-257	Harder	24. 8. 44	Japanese minesweeper off Davol Bay, Luzon, Philippines
SS-273	Robalo	26. 7. 44	Japanese mine off Palawan
SS-275	Runner	6. 43	Japanese mine between Midway and Japan

Pennant No	Name	Date	Course and Location
SS-277	*Scamp*	16. 11. 44	Japanese naval forces east of Tokyo Bay
SS-278	*Scorpion*	1. 44	Japanese mine in Yellow Sea
SS-279	*Snook*	8. 4. 45	Japanese naval forces east of Formosa
SS-284	*Tullibee*	26. 3. 44	Own torpedo off Peliu Island
SS-289	*Capelin*	12. 43	Japanese naval forces north of Celebes
SS-290	*Cisco*	28. 9. 43	Japanese aircraft in Sulu Sea, Mindanao, Philippines
SS-294	*Escolar*	10. 44	Japanese mine in Yellow Sea
SS-306	*Tang*	24. 10. 44	Own torpedo off Formosa

Pennant No	Name	Date	Course and Location
SS-314	*Shark*	24. 10. 44	Japanese naval forces south of Formosa
SS-316	*Barbel*	4. 2. 45	Japanese aircraft off Palawan
SS-332	*Bullhead*	8. 45	Japanese aircraft off Bali
SS-361	*Golet*	14. 6. 44	Japanese naval forces north of Honshu, Japan
SS-369	*Kete*	3. 45	Japanese submarine between Okinawa and Midway
SS-371	*Lagarto*	4. 5. 45	Japanese minelayer in Gulf of Thailand

Submarine Task Forces and Groups During the Second World War

The following survey compiled by Manfred Reinert follows the pattern of similar surveys in earlier books in this series. Although the possibility of minor errors cannot be ruled out, we still rely on the main source, *The History of United States Naval Operations in World War II*, since no more detailed survey exists covering US sources chronologically and materially in relationship to total accounted expenditure.

However, the peculiarities of submarine warfare mean that this table has to be slightly different from those in the earlier books in its descriptions of participation in various theatres of war. Submarines in the Pacific theatre were not directly and permanently attached to carrier battle groups as were cruisers and destroyers, but were deployed to protect surface vessels involved in US landing operations. They were also occasionally used as commando troop transports in landing operations, e.g., in the Aleutians. During the two last years of the War, submarines were organized into independent task forces or task groups responsible to fleet command.

Date	Operation and Unit	Submarines involved (SS nos)
5. 8. 1942	**Atlantic** USN Atlantic Fleet	SUBRON 1: 63, 64, 65, 67, 68, 69, 71, 121, 122, 125, 159, 172, 173, 204, 205 SUBRON 3: 116, 117, 118, 119, 120, 126, 129, 163, 164, 165 SUBRON 7: 78, 79, 81, 82, 83, 84, 86, 87, 88, 89, 90, 91, 92, 93, 95, 97
11/1942	Landing in French Morocco	TG 34.2: 253, 233 TG 34.10: 220 on survey duties
12/1941	**Pacific** Manila Bay and Olongapo	142, 143, 145, 146, 172, 173, 174, 175, 176, 177, 178, 182, 183, 184, 185, 187, 188, 189, 190, 191, 192, 193, 194, 195, 196, 197
12/1941	Philippines region	141, 144
1 + 2/1942	ABDA – Command, TF 3	as in Manila, above, without 146 and 195
5/1943	Capture of Attu, TG 16.5	123, 128, 133, 135, 137, 138, 139, 140, 143, 145, 146, 167, 168
11 + 12/1943	Capture of Gilbert Islands	168, 179, 183, 190, 191, 196, 200, 226, 263, 308
2/1944	Operations in the Marshall Islands	178, 183, 184, 196, 217, 281
2/1944	Operations off Truk, TF 17	183, 196, 212, 227, 247, 281, 305, 306, 309, 312
5/1942	Eastern Australia, TG 42.1	SUBDIV 53 + 201: 142, 143, 144, 145, 146, 153, 154, 155, 156, 157, 158
5/1942	Midway and Hawaii, TG 7.1 TG 7.2 TG 7.3	168, 169, 170, 198, 202, 209, 210, 211, 212, 214, 229 167, 179, 237 173, 175, 215, 230
6/1942	North Pacific Force in the Aleutians, TG 8.5	123, 128, 132, 133, 139, 140
6–8/1942	South Pacific Force in the E. Solomons, TF 42	143, 144, 146, 154, 155, 157
6/1944	Sea battle in the Philippines, TF17	179, 186, 193, 197, 206, 215, 218, 229, 230, 244, 262, 282, 304, 311, 385, 386, 387, 388, 390
6/1944	VII. Fleet	222, 241, 250, 255, 256, 257, 259, 263, 272
10/1944	Pacific Fleet; TF 17	182, 194, 203, 221, 228, 231, 232, 236, 237, 252, 276, 279, 306, 316, 321, 367, 368, 387, 391, 392, 396, 403
10/1944	VII. Fleet; TG 71.1	227, 240, 242, 243, 247, 270, 363
1/1945	Pacific Fleet; TF 17	190, 199, 217, 220, 234, 236, 268, 285, 326, 367, 382, 389, 393, 401, 402, 405, 406, 407, 413
1/1945	VII. Fleet; TG 71.1	240, 242, 243, 245, 252, 254, 274, 313, 315, 316, 321, 322, 323, 327, 363, 365, 370

Submarines as Memorials and Museums

The number of submarines taken over post-War by various institutions as memorials or floating museums is far greater than that of other ships such as carriers, cruisers, destroyers or escort vessels. However, the maintenance of museum pieces is associated with permanently rising costs that often cannot be recovered from entrance fees alone. For this reason some of these boats are in better condition than others. For those in the worst condition, there is the distinct possibility that they will have to close down. The following table is in alphabetical order of name.

Of the modern vessels not covered by this book, *Nautilus* (SSN-571) was in 1985 installed as the first nuclear submarine in the Museum of Naval History at Groton, Connecticut.

American Submarines as Museums and Memorials

Name (ex-Pennant No)	Location	Notes
Batfish (SS-310)	Muskogee, Oklahoma	
Becuna (SS-319)	Philadelphia, Pennsylvania	with the cruiser *Olympia*
Bowfin (SS-287)	Honolulu, Hawaii	
Cavalla (SS-244)	Galveston, Texas	
Clamagore (SS-343)	Charleston, South Carolina	1)
Cobia (SS-245)	Manitowoc, Wisconsin	
Cod (SS-224)	Cleveland, Ohio	
Croaker (AGSS-246)	Groton, Connecticut	2)
Drum (SS-228)	Mobile, Alabama	3)
Ling (AGSS-297)	Hackensack, New Jersey	
Lionfish (SS-298)	Fall River, Massachusetts	4)
Marlin (SST-2)	Omaha, Nebraska	5)
Pampanito (SS-383)	San Francisco, California	
Requin (AGSS-481)	Tampa, Florida	6)
Silversides (AGSS-236)	Chicago, Illinois	
Torsk (AGSS-423)	Baltimore, Maryland	
U 505	Chicago, Illinois	7)
Growler (SSG-577)	New York, New York	8)

Notes
1. With CVS *Yorktown* and DD *Laffey* at the Patriots Point Museum Centre.
2. Towed to Buffalo, NY, in 1989, and established as a museum ship together with CG *Little Rock* and DD *The Sullivans*.
3. With BB *Alabama*.
4. With BB *Massachusetts*, DD *Joseph P. Kennedy* and PT-796.
5. With AM *Hazard*.
6. Returned to the US Navy in 1989 as no longer required by the city of Tampa and has been removed from there.
7. U-boat captured during the War.
8. With CVS *Intrepid* and DD *Edson*.

Cod (SS-224), now a floating museum at Cleveland Ohio, July 1982 [LvG]

Drum (SS-228) lies in Battleship Park, Mobile, Alabama, directly behind the battleship Alabama (BB-60), February 1982. [GGh]

Midships detail of Drum, now lying high in the water, 12 April 1984. [HM]

Bowfin (SS-287) is now a floating museum at Pearl Harbor, Honolulu, Hawaii, July 1981. [LvG]

Separated from the open water by the cruiser *Olympia* ('Cruiser 6', now IX-40), *Becuna* is moored as a museum boat at Philadelphia. [J. Hummel]

Clamagore (SS-343), a GUPPY III, now serves as a floating museum at Patriots Point historical centre in Charleston, SC. The photograph was taken from the flight deck of the aircraft carrier *Yorktown* (latterly CVS-10) on 5 October 1988. In the background is *Laffey* (DD-724), the last active FRAM II-DD. [Te]

This and the next photograph, of *Pampanito* (SS-383), were taken near Fisherman's Wharf, San Francisco on 16 October 1988 during the 1988 Navy Days. There is a 5in L/25 gun on the fore deck, an unshielded 20mm AA gun on the forward cigarette deck, with a 40mm Bofors mounted on the after cigarette deck. There is an SJ antenna on its own conical mast, and a later SS antenna on the slimmer support. [Te]

The Fleet Snorkel *Torsk* (ex-AGSS-423) as a floating museum at Baltimore, Md, 2 July 1987 [MW]

The four-times reclassified *Requin* (AGSS-481) had been a floating museum at Tampa, Florida, but was relocated in 1989. In this photograph 26 December 1988, the diving planes are extended. [P&L Collection]

On 25 May 1989 *Growler* (SSG-577) was installed as a museum boat in New York. She lies at Pier 89, opposite the aircraft carrier *Intrepid* (ex CVS-11), from which this photograph was taken on 24 May 1989. [CW]

Bibliography

Books

J. D. Alden: **The Fleet Submarine in the U.S. Navy,** United States Naval Institute Press, Annapolis, USA 1979

ibid.: **U.S. Submarine Attacks during World War Two,** United States Naval Institute Press, Annapolis, USA 1989

Conway's All the World's Fighting Ships 1860-1982, Vol. I-IV, edited by R. Gardiner, Conway Maritime Press, London 1975-1985

W. H. Cracknell: USS Barb (SS-220), Warship Profile Series, Windsor, England 1973

Dictionary of American Naval Fighting Ships, Vol. I-VIII, edited from Naval Historical Center, Washington, USA 1959-1981

J. Fahey: The Ships and Aircraft of the U.S. Fleet, Vols/U.S. Naval Institute Press, I-VIII, 1939-1965

J. Rowe/S. Morison: The Ships and Aircraft of the U.S. Fleet (formerly 'Fahey'), IX + X, U.S. Naval Institute Press, Annapolis, USA 1972 + 1975

N. Friedman: Naval Radar, U.S. Naval Institute Press, Annapolis, USA 1981

ibid.: **U.S. Naval Weapons,** U.S. Naval Institute Press, Annapolis. USA 1983

D. L. Kimble: Chronology of U.S. Navy Submarine Operations in the Pacific 1939-1942. International Graphics Corp., Bennington, USA 1982

P. Law: Shipboard Antennas, Artech House Inc. Dedham, USA 1983

H. Lenton: American Submarines, Macdonald, London, England 1973

A. Lott/R. F. Sumrall: USS Bowfin (SS-287), Leeward Publications, Annapolis, USA 1975

S. E. Morison: History of United States Naval Operations, Vol. I-XV, Little, Brown and Co., Boston, USA 1947-1960

H. E. Musgrove: U.S. Naval Ships Data arranged by Hull Classification, Vol. I-IV, Florissant, USA 1975/1987

Office of Naval Intelligence (Ed.): **U.S. Naval Vessels (ONI-222 Series),** Arms & Armour Press, London, England 1986 and The Floating Drydock, Kressgeville, USA

J. Rowe/S. Morison: Warships of the U.S. Navy, Jane's Publishing, London, England 1983

P. Silverstone: U.S. Warships of World War II, Ian Allan, London, England 1965

ibid.: **U.S. Warships of World War I,** Ian Allan, London, England 1970

ibid.: **U.S. Warships since 1945,** U.S. Naval Institute Press, Annapolis, USA 1987

L. Sowinski/Th. Walkowiak: United States Camouflage of the WW II era, Vol. I + II, The Floating Drydock, Kressgeville, USA 1976-1977

R. C. Stern: U.S. Subs in action, Squadron/Signal Publications, Corrolton, USA 1979

Submarine Force Library & Museum Ass., Inc.: United States Submarine Data Book, Groton, USA 1976

S. Terzibaschitsch: Die Schiffe und Flugzeuge der US-Flotte, J. F. Lehmanns Verlag, Munich 1966

ibid.: **Das FRAM-Modernisierungsprogramm der US-Navy,** Wehrwissenschaftliche Berichte Band 17, J. F. Lehmanns Verlag, Munich 1975

ibid.: **Seemacht USA,** 2 Bände, Bernard & Graefe Verlag, Bonn/Coblenz 1982

ibid.: **Jahrbuch der U.S. Navy,** 3 Bände, Bernard & Graefe Verlag, Coblenz, 1986, 1987, 1988

ibid.: **Kreuzer der U.S. Navy,** Koehlers Verlagsgesellschaft, Herford 1984

ibid.: **Zerstörer der U. S. Navy,** Koehlers Verlagsgesellschaft, Herford 1986

ibid.: **Geleitschiffe der U.S. Navy,** Koehlers Verlagsgesellschaft, Herford 1988

A. J. Watts: Allied Submarines WW II Fact Files, Macdonald and Jane's, London, England 1977

Th. F. Walkowiak: Fleet Submarines of World War Two, Pictorial Histories Publishing Co., Missoula, USA 1988

B. Weddertz: Dictionary of Naval Abbreviations, U.S. Naval Institute Press, Annapolis, USA 1970 and 1986

A. Wetterhahn: Flotten-Revue 1948, 2 Bände, seinerzeitiger Vertrieb P. Schmalenbach, Bremen 1948-1949

Annuals and Reference Books

Data on publisher and frequency given individually

Combat Fleets of the World, Naval Institute Press, Annapolis, Md.; Bi-annual

Flottes de Combat, Editions Maritimes et d'Outre-Mer, Paris; Bi-annual

Jane's Fighting Ships, Jane's Publishing Co., London; Annual

Jane's Weapon Systems, Jane's Publishing Co., London: Annual

N. Polmar: The Ships and Aircraft of the U.S. Fleet, Naval Institute Press, Annapolis, Md.; Every three years

Weyers Flottentaschenbuch, bis Ausgabe 1943/44 Weyers Taschenbuch der Kriegsflotten, Bernard und Graefe Verlag, Koblenz; Bi-annual. (Since 1977/8 available in German and English)

Journals and Periodicals

Title, editor, publisher and frequency of journals consulted in the compilation of this book.

U.S. Naval Institute Proceedings, U.S. Naval Institute, Annapolis, USA. Monthly

Marine-Rundschau, Mönch-Verlag Bonn, Erscheinungsfolge: bi-monthly: discontinued 1990.

Nachrichten aus der U.S. Navy, Herausgeber: S. Terzibaschitsch (Eigenvertrieb), Leonberg. Quarterly

Navy Times, Army Times Publishing Co., Springfield, USA. Weekly

International Defence Review, Jane's Information Group, Bern, Switzerland. Monthly

Warship, Conway Maritime Press, London, England. Quarterly, discontinued 1989

Warship International, International Naval Research Organization, Toledo, USA. Quarterly.

Name Index

Where only a number is given in the following alphabetical list, it refers to an 'SS' category; for other boats the category letters are indicated. The page number refers to the appropriate A Table; class lead boats are given in italics.

SS	Name	Page
A		
218	Albacore	74
AGSS-569	Albacore	125
219	Amberjack	74
522	Amberjack	108
240	Angler	76
308	Apogon	91
311	Archerfish	92
(166)	*Argonaut*	45
475	Argonaut	106
309	Aspro	91
403	Atule	98
B		
285	*Balao*	90
385	Bang	96
220	Barb	74
316	Barbel	92
580	*Barbel*	133
317	Barbero	92
163	*Barracuda*	42
SSK-1	*Barracuda*	121
241	Bashaw	76
164	Bass	42
SSK-2	Bass	121
310	Batfish	91
318	Baya	92
319	Becuna	92
320	Bergall	93
321	Besugo	93
286	Billfish	90
322	Blackfin	93
221	Blackfish	74
324	Blenny	93
325	Blower	93
326	Blueback	93
581	Blueback	133

SS	Name	Page
222	Bluefish	74
242	Bluegill	76
327	Boarfish	93
223	Bonefish	74
582	Bonefish	133
165	Bonita	42
SSK-3	Bonita	121
287	Bowfin	90
243	Bream	76
330	Brill	93
331	Bugara	93
332	Bullhead	93
333	Bumper	93
312	Burrfish	92
C		
334	Cabezon	94
288	Cabrilla	90
170	*Cachalot*	50
323	Caiman	93
289	Capelin	90
336	Capitaine	94
337	Carbonero	94
338	Carp	94
339	Catfish	94
244	Cavalla	76
225	Cero	75
328	Charr	93
341	Chivo	94
342	Chopper	93
329	Chub	93
290	Cisco	90
343	Clamagore	94
344	Cobbler	94
245	Cobia	76
345	Cochino	94
224	Cod	74

SS	Name	Page
477	Conger	106
346	Corporal	94
435	Corsair	106
226	Corvina	75
291	Crevalle	90
246	Croaker	77
347	Cubera	94
348	Cusk	95
478	Cutlass	107
171	Cuttlefish	50
D		
247	Dace	77
227	Darter	75
576	*Darter*	119
335	Dentuda	94
292	Devilfish	90
479	Diablo	107
349	Diodon	95
350	Dogfish	95
169	Dolphin	49
AGSS-555	*Dolphin*	136
248	Dorado	77
293	Dragonet	90
228	Drum	75
E		
340	Entemedor	94
294	Escolar	90
F		
230	Finback	75
249	Flasher	77
250	Flier	77
251	Flounder	77
229	Flying Fish	75

SS	Name	Page
G		
252	Gabilan	77
206	Gar	64
212	*Gato*	74
361	Golet	79
207	Grampus	64
523	Grampus	108
208	Grayback	64
SSG-574	*Grayback*	131
209	Grayling	64
351	Greenfish	95
213	Greenling	74
210	Grenadier	64
525	Grenadier	108
214	Grouper	74
215	Growler	74
SSG-577	*Growler*	131
216	Grunion	74
217	Guardfish	74
362	Guavina	80
211	Gudgeon	64
567	Gudgeon	114
363	Guitarro	80
253	Gunnel	77
254	Gurnard	77
H		
295	Hackleback	90
256	Hake	77
352	Halfbeak	95
232	Halibut	75
255	Haddo	77
231	Haddock	75
364	Hammerhead	80
257	Harder	77
568	Harder	114
365	Hardhead	95
366	Hawkbill	95
233	Herring	75
258	Hoe	77
I		
367	Icefish	95
482	Irex	107
J		
259	Jack	77
368	Jallao	95

SS	Name	Page
K		
369	Kete	95
234	Kingfish	75
370	Kraken	95
L		
371	Lagarto	95
372	Lamprey	95
296	Lancetfish	90
260	Lapon	78
297	Ling	90
298	Lionfish	91
373	Lizardfish	96
374	Loggerhead	96
M		
375	Macabi	96
204	Mackerel	67
SST-1	*Mackerel*	123
299	Manta	91
376	Mapiro	96
205	Marlin	67
SST-2	Marlin	123
480	Medregal	107
377	Menhaden	96
378	Mero	96
261	Mingo	78
300	Moray	91
262	Muskallunge	78
N		
167	*Narwhal*	47
168	Nautilus	47
O		
63	*O-2*	31
64	O-3	31
65	O-4	31
67	O-6	31
68	O-7	31
69	O-8	31
70	O-9	31
71	O-10	31
484	Odax	107
P		
263	Paddle	78
383	Pampanito	96
384	Parche	96
264	Pargo	78

SS	Name	Page
176	Perch	54
313	Perch	92
178	Permit	54
265	Peto	78
177	Pickerel	54
524	Pickerel	108
382	Picuda	96
173	Pike	53
386	Pilotfish	96
387	Pintado	97
388	Pipefish	97
409	Piper	98
389	Piranha	97
390	Plaice	97
179	Plunger	54
266	Pogy	78
180	Pollack	54
486	Pomodon	107
181	Pompano	54
391	Pomphret	97
267	Pompon	78
172	*Porpoise*	53
268	Puffer	78
Q		
393	Queenfish	97
424	Quillback	106
R		
78	*R-1*	33
79	R-2	33
80	R-3	33
81	R-4	33
82	R-5	33
83	R-6	33
84	R-7	33
86	R-9	33
87	R-10	33
88	R-11	33
89	R-12	33
90	R-13	33
91	R-14	33
92	R-15	33
93	R-16	33
94	R-17	33
95	R-18	33
96	R-19	33
97	R-20	33
269	Rasher	78
270	Raton	78

SS	Name	Page
271	Ray	78
394	Razorback	97
272	Redfin	78
395	Redfish	97
487	Remora	107
481	Requin	107
273	Robalo	79
274	Rock	79
301	Roncador	91
396	Ronquil	97
275	Runner	79
476	Runner	106

S

SS	Name	Page
105	*S-1*	35
123	S-18	35
125	S-20	35
126	S-21	35
127	S-22	35
128	S-23	35
129	S-24	35
130	S-25	35
131	S-26	35
132	S-27	35
133	S-28	35
134	S-29	36
135	S-30	36
136	S-31	36
137	S-32	36
138	S-33	36
139	S-34	36
140	S-35	36
141	S-36	36
142	S-37	36
143	S-38	36
144	S-39	36
145	S-40	36
146	S-41	36
116	*S-11*	37
117	S-12	37
118	S-13	37
119	S-14	37
120	S-15	37
121	S-16	37
122	S-17	37
153	*S-42*	38
154	S-43	38
155	S-44	38
156	S-45	38

SS	Name	Page
157	S-46	38
158	S-47	38
159	*S-48*	39
302	Sabalo	91
303	Sablefish	91
192	Sailfish	60
SSR-572	Sailfish	128
182	*Salmon*	57
SSR-573	Salmon	128
381	Sand Lance	96
488	Sarda	107
188	*Sargo*	60
189	Saury	60
276	Sawfish	79
397	Scabbardfish	97
277	Scamp	79
278	Scorpion	79
191	Sculpin	60
399	Sea Cat	97
400	Sea Devil	98
401	Sea Dog	98
194	Seadragon	60
402	Sea Fox	98
304	Seahorse	91
183	Seal	57
483	Sea Leopard	107
195	Sealion	60
315	Sealion	92
405	Sea Owl	98
406	Sea Poacher	98
196	Searaven	60
407	Sea Robin	98
197	Seawolf	60
398	Segundo	97
408	Sennet	98
235	Shad	75
174	*Shark*	55
314	Shark	92
236	Silversides	75
485	Sirago	107
305	Skate	91
184	Skipjack	57
185	Snapper	57
279	Snook	79
411	Spadefish	98
190	Spearfish	60
404	Spikefish	98
489	Spinax	107
413	Spot	99
414	Springer	99

SS	Name	Page
192	Squalus	60
280	Steelhead	79
392	Sterlet	97
415	Stickleback	99
186	Stingray	57
197	Sturgeon	57
281	Sunfish	79
193	Swordfish	60

T

SS	Name	Page
198	*Tambor*	64
306	Tang	91
563	*Tang*	114
175	Tarpon	55
199	Tautog	64
417	Tench	106
410	Threadfin	98
200	Thresher	64
418	Thornback	106
419	Tigrone	106
307	Tilefish	91
283	Tinosa	79
420	Tirante	106
416	Tiru	99
422	Toro	106
423	Torsk	106
412	Trepang	98
237	Trigger	75
564	Trigger	114
201	Triton	64
202	Trout	64
566	Trout	114
425	Trumpetfish	99
421	Trutta	106
284	Tullibee	79
203	Tuna	64
282	Tunny	79
426	Tusk	99

V

SS	Name	Page
490	Volador	108

W

SS	Name	Page
238	Wahoo	75
565	Wahoo	114
239	Whale	76

214

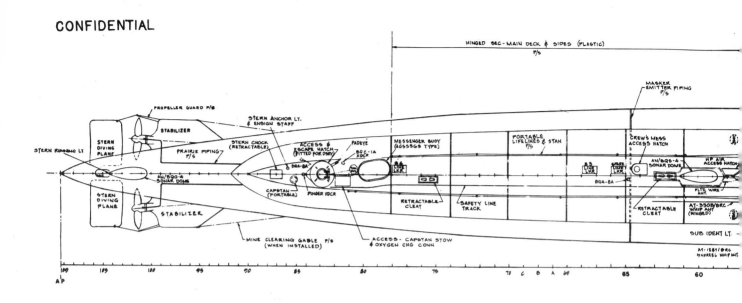

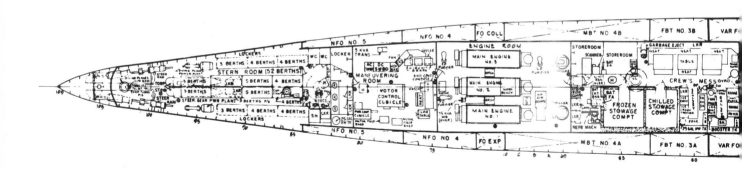

Over the years, the US Navy has released some 'Confidential' classified drawings from the Pearl Harbor Naval Shipyard. Four drawings from the *Tang*-Class (SS-563) file have been selected as examples.

Top: plan view Bottom: section through platform deck. (source: US Navy)